J. W. FISKE

J. W. FISKE
1893

Copper Weathervanes, Bannerets,
Lightning Rods, Stable Fixtures

Illustrated Catalog and Historical Introduction

AMERICAN HISTORICAL CATALOG COLLECTION

THE PYNE PRESS
Princeton

Note to the Reader. Reproduction of copy and line drawings are as faithful to the original as is technically possible. Broken type and lines which are uneven or broken can be spotted; these are original! You will understand that manufacturers of such products as woodenware, tinware, glassware and weathervanes were not dedicated to the fine art of printing or involved in the business of publishing. All American Historical Catalog Collection editions are photographed in facsimile from the best available copy, are printed on an especially receptive offset paper, and are strongly bound.

Illustrated Catalogue and Price List

—OF—

Copper Weather Vanes,

——MANUFACTURED BY——

J. W. FISKE,

39 AND 41 PARK PLACE,

NEW YORK.

The OLDEST AND MOST EXTENSIVE MANUFACTURER of Vanes in the United States; no other person having been engaged in manufacturing this class of goods but a few years. In consequence of my long experience in this line of business, I am prepared to offer dealers and consumers a decided advantage both in price and quality. My Vanes are all MADE of COPPER and not a combination of zinc and copper, like other Vanes in the market. Am continually adding NEW AND ORIGINAL DESIGNS to my stock, which now comprises the LARGEST AND FINEST ASSORT-MENT IN THE COUNTRY, for which I have received MEDALS AND DIPLOMAS over all other exhibitors, from the principal Fairs and Institutions. My Vanes are made of COPPER, GILDED WITH THE FINEST GOLD LEAF; will not corrode, and will keep bright a long time. Every Vane is a PERFECT INDICATOR OF THE WIND, and warranted in every respect superior to anything in the market. The letters and balls are well gilded. The Spires are wrought iron, with hardened steel spindles for the Vanes to turn upon. I would call especial attention to my Eagles, which are full-bodied, and wings double thickness, a PERFECT FAC-SIMILE OF THE AMERICAN EAGLE taken from life.

The price of each Vane includes a wrought iron Spire, with points of compass, gilt letters and balls.

It is impossible with the large variety and constant additions to illustrate but comparatively a small portion of my different designs of which I manufacture.

☞**Vanes of any design made to order at short notice and at reasonable rates.**

I would caution my customers and the public against being deceived by Vanes which are now being made, copied after my designs, some of which are made of SHEET ZINC, AND COVERED WITH A THIN SOLUTION OF COPPER WITH ZINC TUBING. Unlike my Vanes, which are made of Sheet Copper, and mounted with brass tubing.

☞**Purchase no Vanes unless made of Sheet Copper, or Brass, and mounted on Brass Tubing.**

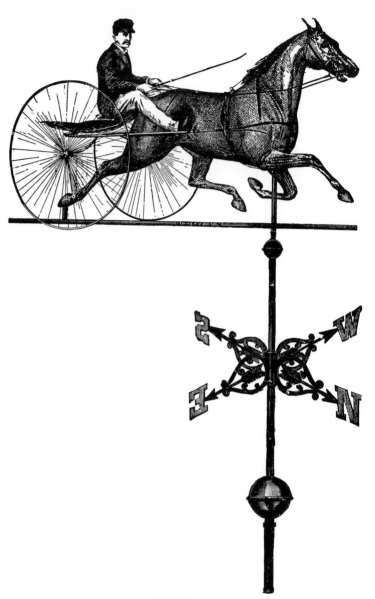

MAUD S.

Design Patented, February, 1881.

No. 346. New Design, full-bodied, 36 inches long $42 00
"   347.   "   "   "   "   with Sulky and Driver 60 00
"   348.   "   "   "   "   31 inches long 25 00

Copyrighted, 1881.

☞ All my Vanes are of copper, and gilded with gold leaf.

ST. JULIAN.

Design Patented, February, 1881.

No. 349.   New Design, full-bodied, 39 inches long $44 00
" 350.   "   "   "   "   with Sulky and Driver 62 00
" 351.   "   "   ¾ "   "   32 inches long 26 00

Copyrighted, 1881.

☞ All my Vanes are of copper, and gilded with gold leaf.

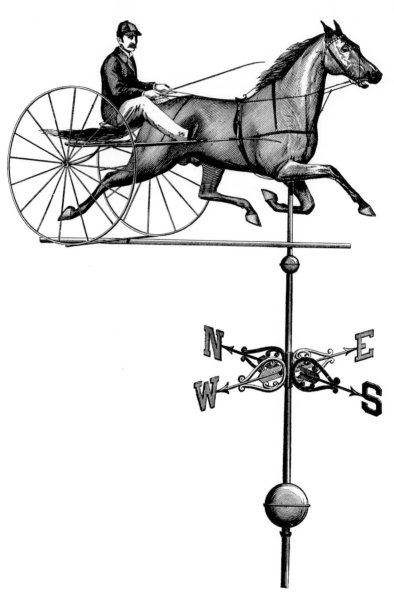

ALCRYON.

No. 505. Full-bodied, 36 inches long _____$55 00
" 506.   "   "   42   "   "   including Sulky and Driver _____ 75 00

Copyrighted, 1893.

☞ All my Vanes are of copper, and gilded with gold leaf.

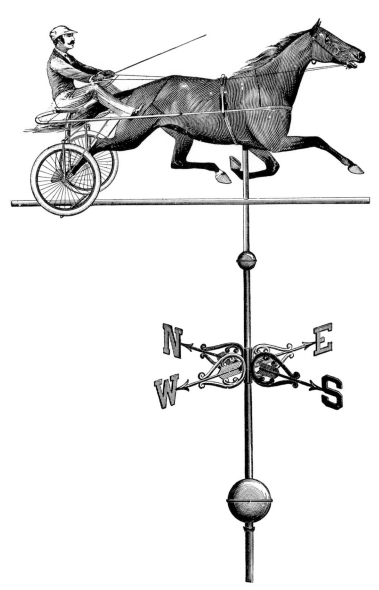

NANCY HANKS WITH PNEUMATIC TIRE SULKY.

o. 507. Full-bodied, 36 inches long _____ $55 00

' 508.   "   "   42   "   "   including Sulky and Driver _____ 75 00

Copyrighted 1893.

☞ All my Vanes are of copper, and gilded with gold leaf.

DEXTER.

☞ All my Vanes are of copper, and gilded with gold leaf.

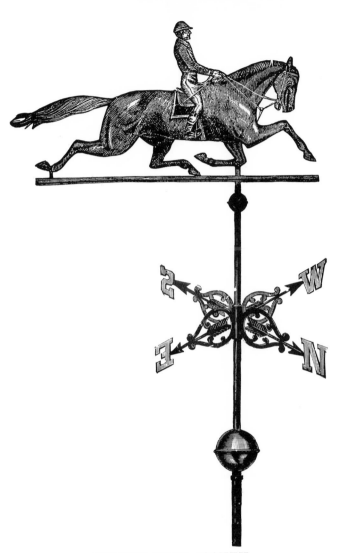

DEXTER WITH JOCKEY.

No. B3. New Design, full-bodied, 41 inches long _$50 00
"   B3.   "   "   "   "   41   "   " with Jockey _ _ _ _ _ _ _ _ _ _ _ _ _ _ _ _ 65 00
"   B3.   "   "   "   "   with Sulky and Driver _ _ _ _ _ _ _ _ _ _ _ _ _ _ _ 75 00

☞ All my Vanes are of copper, and gilded with gold leaf.

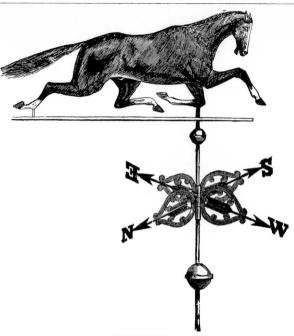

DEXTER.

No. 6.   30 inches long_____$22 0
  "   7.   With Sulky and Driver_____ 32 0
  "   8.   "   Wagon and Driver_____ 40 0

DEXTER.

No. A3.   New Pattern, full-bodied, 24 inches long_____$25 0
  "   A3.   "   "   "   " · 24   "   " with Jockey_____ 30 0
  "   A3.   "   "   "   "   with Sulky and Driver _____ 35 0

☞ All my Vanes are of copper, and gilded with gold leaf.

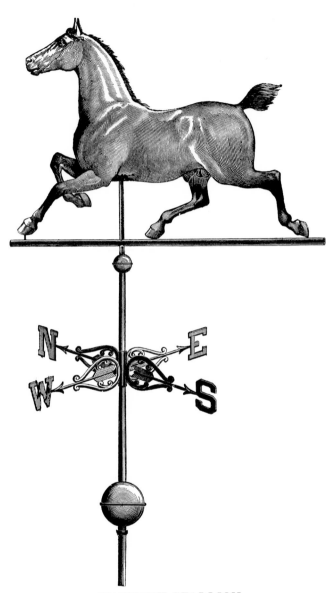

HACKNEY STALLION.

No. 512.	¾ Full-bodied, 24 inches long	....	$50 00
" 512½.	¾ " " 30 " "	....	70 00
" 513.	¾ " " 48 " "	....	180 00

Copyrighted 1893.

☞ All my Vanes are of copper, and gilded with gold leaf.

SADDLE HORSE AND LADY RIDER.

No. 519.   ¾ Full-bodied, 30 inches long, mounted complete as shown on page 9 _ _ $80 00
ANY SIZE MADE TO ORDER.
Copyrighted 1893.

RUNNING HORSE AND JOCKEY WITH BANGED TAIL.

No. 515.   Full-bodied, 31 inches long, mounted complete as shown on page 9 _ _ _ _ $30 00
Copyrighted 1893.

HORSE OVER FENCE.

No. 15.   New Design, full-bodied, 31 in. long, mounted complete as shown on page 9, $25 00
☞ All my Vanes are of copper, and gilded with gold leaf.

SADDLE HORSE AND RIDER.

o. 516. ¾ Full-bodied, 31 inches long, mounted complete as shown on page 9 __$80 00

Copyrighted 1893.

RUNNING HORSE AND JOCKEY.

o. 19.   Full-bodied, 31 inches long, mounted complete as shown on page 9 _ _ _ _ _$30 00

Copyrighted 1893.

☞ All my Vanes are of copper, and gilded with gold leaf.

HACKNEY TO CART.

No. 514.   ¾ Full-bodied, 42 inches long, including cart and driver, mounted com-
plete as shown on page 14 _$100

Copyrighted 1893.

CIVILIAN.

No. 20.   32 inches long, mounted complete as shown on page 14 _ _ _ _ _ _ _ _ _ _ _ _ _ _ _$35

☞ All my Vanes are of copper, and gilded with gold leaf.

HORSE OVER HURDLE.

No. 517.   ¾ Full-bodied, 30 inches long, mounted complete as shown on page 14__$90 00

ANY SIZE MADE TO ORDER.

Copyrighted 1893.

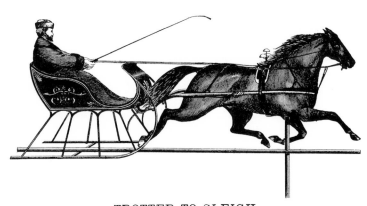

TROTTER TO SLEIGH.

No. 511.   ¾ Full-bodied, 41 inches long, mounted complete as shown on page 14__$75 00

Copyrighted 1893.

☞ All my Vanes are of copper, and gilded with gold leaf.

ETHAN ALLEN.

No. 9.   ¾ Full-bodied, 31 inches long _____$20 00

Copyrighted 1893.

TEAM TROTTERS TO ROAD WAGON.

No. 510.   ¾ Full-bodied, 45 inches long, mounted complete as shown above_____$100 00

Copyrighted 1893.

☞ All my Vanes are of copper, and gilded with gold leaf.

MOUNTAIN BOY.

o. 12.   Full-bodied, 33 inches long _$36 00

Copyrighted 1893.

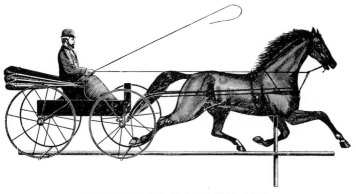

TROTTER TO ROAD WAGON.

o. 509.   ¾ Full-bodied, 44 inches long, mounted complete as shown above _ _ _ _ _ _$80 00

Copyrighted 1893.

☞ All my Vanes are of copper, and gilded with gold leaf.

GOLDSMITH MAID.

No. 202.   New Design, full-bodied, 32 inches long _____$30 0
"   203.   "   "   "   "   with Sulky and Driver _____ 45 0
"   204.   "   "   "   "   "   Wagon and Driver_____ 50 0

HORSE OVER BALL.

No. 14.   New Design, full-bodied, 31 inches long, mounted complete as above__$25 0

☞ All my Vanes are of copper, and gilded with gold leaf.

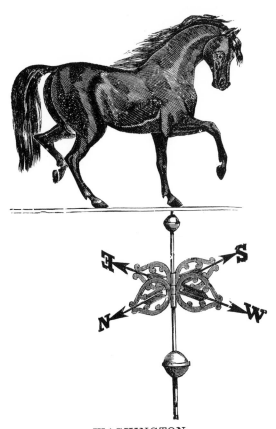

WASHINGTON.

No. 16.   New Design, full-bodied, 33 inches long --------------------------------$60 00

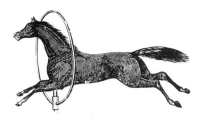

HORSE AND HOOP.

No. 13.   New Design, full-bodied, 31 inches long, mounted complete as above--$25 00

☞ All my Vanes are of copper, and gilded with gold leaf.

ETHAN ALLEN, Jr.

No. 200. ¾ Full-bodied, 26 inches long _____ _____$15 0

ETHAN ALLEN.

No. A9.   Full-bodied, 26 inches long _____$25 00

Copyrighted, 1893.

☞ All my Vanes are of copper, and gilded with gold leaf.

BLACK HAWK.

No. 201.   26 inches long - $17 00

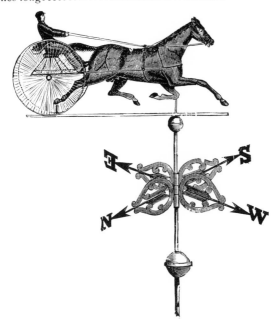

ETHAN ALLEN WITH SULKY.

No. 10.   36 inches long - $30 00

☞ All my Vanes are of copper, and gilded with gold leaf.

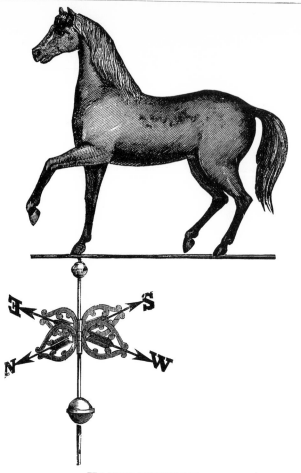

HAMBLETONIAN.
No. 345. ¾ Full-bodied, 26 inches long $25 00

ARABIAN.
No. 21. 17 inches long, mounted complete as shown above.....................$14 00
☞ All my Vanes are of copper, and gilded with gold leaf.

BULL.

o. 327.   Full-bodied, 28 inches long _$50 00

☞ All my Vanes are of copper, and gilded with gold leaf.

COW. (Duchess of Oneida).

Design Patented, April, 1880.

No. 326.   Full-bodied, 42 inches long $120

☞ All my Vanes are of copper, and gilded with gold leaf.

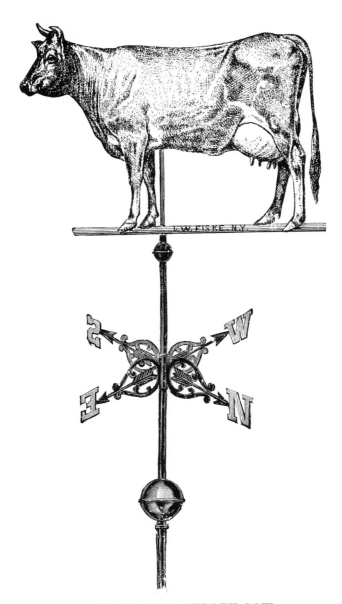

SHORT HORNED JERSEY COW.

No. A30.   Full-bodied, 34 inches long _____ $ 65 00

"   326¼.   "   "   48   "   "   _____ 125 00

☞ All my Vanes are of copper, and gilded with gold leaf.

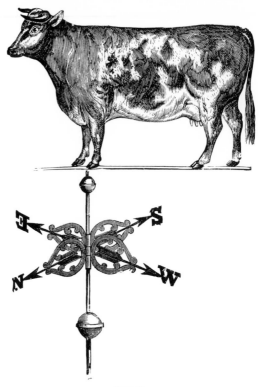

COW.

No. 30.	Full-bodied, 28 inches long	$40 00
" 30½. ¾ "	" 28 " "	30 00
" 31. ½ "	" 24 " "	20 00
" 31. ½ "	" 28 " "	22 50

ENGLISH HOUND.

No. 69.   33 inches long, mounted complete as shown above $38 00

☞ All my Vanes are of copper, and gilded with gold leaf.

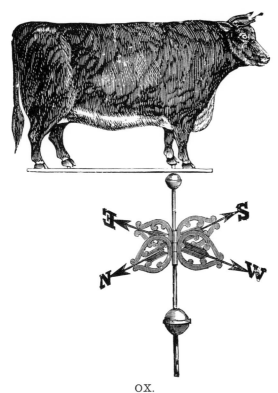

OX.

No. 33½ ¾ Full-bodied, 28 inches long _____$30 00
" 34.   ½ "   "   24   "   "   _____ 20 00
" 34½ ½ "   "   28   "   "   _____ 22 50

DOG.

No. 344. 33 inches long, mounted complete as shown above_____$25 00

☞ All my Vanes are of copper, and gilded with gold leaf.

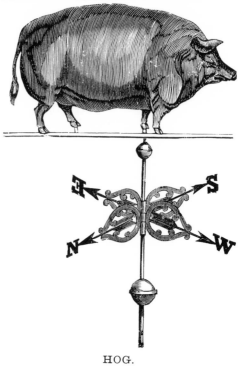

HOG.

No. 38.   ¾ Full-bodied, 34 inches long _____$36 00
"   39.   ¾   "   "   40   "   "   _____ 60 00

MERINO RAM, SWEEPSTAKES.

No. 23.   30 inches long, mounted complete as shown above_____$32 00

☞ All my Vanes are of copper, and gilded with gold leaf.

SHEEP.

No. 22.   ¾ Full-bodied, 28 inches long _____ $25 00

MERINO RAM, ETHAN ALLEN.

No. 24.   36 inches long, mounted complete as shown above _____ $50 00

☞ All my Vanes are of copper, and gilded with gold leaf.

DRAGON.

No. 531. ¾ Full-bodied, 3 feet 6 inches long, mounted complete as shown on
page 27 _____$130 00

Copyrighted 1893.

ANY SIZE MADE TO ORDER.

DRAGON.

No. 74. 54 inches long, mounted complete as shown on page 27_____$60 00

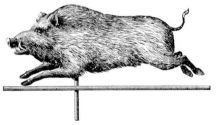

BOAR.

No. 522. ¾ Full-bodied, 30 inches long, mounted complete as shown on page 27__$40 00

Copyrighted 1893.

☞ All my Vanes are of copper, and gilded with gold leaf.

ELEPHANT.

. 75. 28 inches long, mounted complete as shown on page 27 _____ $40 00
76. 34   "   "   "   "   "   "   27 _____ 60 00

LION.

. 78. 3 feet long, mounted complete as shown on page 27 _____ $ 80 00
79. 4 "   "   "   "   "   "   27 _____ 125 00

BUFFALO.

o. 520. ¾ Full-bodied, 34 inches long, mounted complete as shown on page 27 __ $65 00

Copyrighted 1893.

☞ All my Vanes are of copper, and gilded with gold leaf.

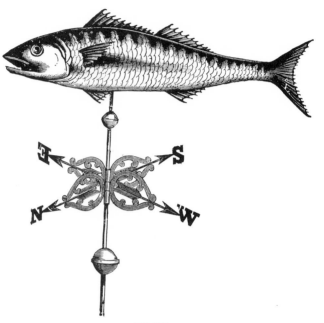

FISH.

No. 61½. Full-bodied, 30 inches long .... $30 (
"   62½.   "   "   38   "   "   .... 40 (

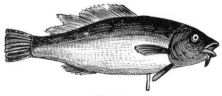

FISH.

No. 61. 24 inches long, mounted complete as shown above .... $17 5(
"   62. 30   "   "   "   "   "   "   .... 20 0(
Fish for Swinging Signs, 9 inches long .... 3 0(
"   "   "   "   16   "   "   .... 4 0(

☞ All my Vanes are of copper, and gilded with gold leaf.

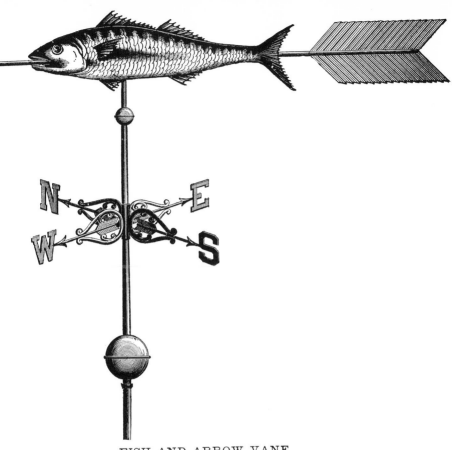

FISH AND ARROW VANE.

No. 539.   Fish, full-bodied, 30 inches long, arrow 5 feet long_ _ _ _ _ _ _ _ _ _ _ _ _ _ _ _ _ _$65 00

Copyrighted 1893.

SWAN.

No. 40.   27 inches long, mounted complete as shown above _ _ _ _ _ _ _ _ _ _ _ _ _ _ _ _ _ _$40 00

ANY SIZE MADE TO ORDER.

☞ All my Vanes are of copper, and gilded with gold leaf.

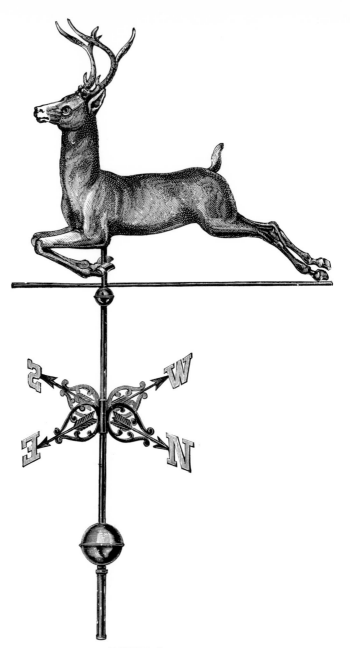

RUNNING DEER.

No. 222.   Full-bodied, 50 inches long_____$90 00
"   223.   "   "   36   "   "   _____ 50 00
"   224.   "   "   20   "   "   _____ 30 00

☞ All my Vanes are of copper, and gilded with gold leaf.

DEER AND HOUND.

No. 64. 60 inches long, mounted complete as shown on page 32 _____ $40 00
" 65. 50 " " " " " 32 _____ 35 00
" 63. 30 " " " " " 32, without hound_ 20 00

STANDING DEER.

No. 60. 29 inches high, mounted complete as shown on page 32 _____ $25 00

☞ All my Vanes are of copper, and gilded with gold leaf.

CROWING ROOSTER.

No. 330.   Full-bodied, 21 inches high including ball and arrow, with 2 feet arrow, $38 00

Copyrighted, 1893.

FOX.

No. 70.   30 inches long, mounted complete as shown above _____$33 00

ANY SIZE MADE TO ORDER.

☞ All my Vanes are of copper, and gilded with gold leaf.

CROWING ROOSTER.

No. 331.   Full-bodied, 21 inches high, including ball and arrow, with 2 feet arrow, $34 00

Copyrighted 1893.

BEAR.

No. 518.   ¾ Full-bodied, 28 inches long, mounted complete as shown above------$40 00

Copyrighted 1893.

☞ All my Vanes are of copper, and gilded with gold leaf.

GAME ROOSTER.

No. 523.   ¾ Full-bodied, 18 inches high, with 2 feet arrow____ _____$25 00

Copyrighted 1893.

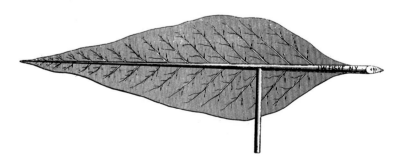

TOBACCO LEAF.

No. 399.   4 feet long, mounted complete as shown above_____$35 00

☞ All my Vanes are of copper, and gilded with gold leaf.

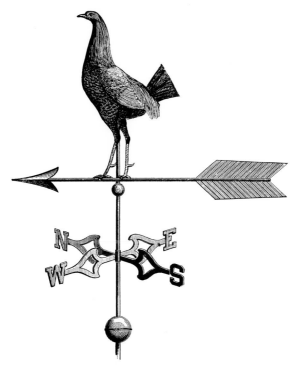

GAME ROOSTER IN FIGHTING TRIM.

No. 521. ¾ Full-bodied, 18 inches high, with 2 feet arrow_____$25 00

Copyrighted 1893.

CIGAR.

No. 525. 36 inches long, mounted complete as shown above _____$30 00

Copyrighted, 1893.

☞ All my Vanes are of copper, and gilded with gold leaf.

ROOSTER.

No. 332.	¾ Full-bodied, 13 inches high					$ 7 50
" 333.	¾	"	"	24	"	"	15 00
" 334.	¾	"	"	28	"	"	25 00
" 335.	¾	"	"	36	"	"	35 00

☞ All my Vanes are of copper, and gilded with gold leaf.

ROOSTER AND ARROW.

No. 341. ¾ Full-bodied, 15 inches high, with 18 inches arrow_____$14 00

" 342. ¾ " " 26 " " " 2 feet 6 inches arrow_____ 30 00

" 343. ¾ " " 32 " " " 3 feet arrow_____ 40 00

☞ All my Vanes are of copper, and gilded with gold leaf.

ROOSTER AND ARROW.

No. 338. ¾ Full-bodied, 18 inches high, with 2 feet arrow ------------------------$16 00
" 339. ¾ "   "   18   "   "   "   2 feet 6 inches arrow--------------- 20 00

GAME ROOSTER.

No. 340. ½ Full-bodied, 18 inches high --$10 0
" 340½ ¾ "   "   18   "   "   -------------------- ----------------- 12 0

☞ All my Vanes are of copper, and gilded with gold leaf.

PIGEON ON BALL, WITH ARROW.

No. 329.   New Design, full-bodied, 18 inches high, including ball and arrow, with
2 feet arrow _$20 00

OWL.

No. 524.   ¾ Full-bodied, 18 inches high, with broom 3 feet long, mounted complete
as shown above _$60 00

Copyrighted, 1893.

☞ All my Vanes are of copper, and gilded with gold leaf.

PIGEON ON BALL, WITH ARROW.

No. 328.   New Design, full-bodied, 18 inches high, including ball and arrow, with
2 feet arrow _____$28 00

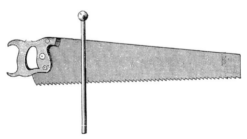

SAW.

No. 526.   36 inches long, mounted complete as shown above_____$35 00

Copyrighted 1893.

☞ All my Vanes are of copper, and gilded with gold leaf.

EAGLE AND SCROLL.

No. 317.   Eagle, 2 feet 3 inches, spread, with 4 feet scroll _____ $ 45 00
"   318.   "   3 "   spread, with 5 feet scroll_____ 75 00
"   319.   "   4 "   "   "   6 "   "   _____ 100 00

☞ All my Vanes are of copper, and gilded with gold leaf.

EAGLE AND SCROLL.

No. 57.	Is No. 56 Eagle, with 3 feet scroll						$26 00
" 58.	" " 55	"	" 3½ "	"			33 00
" 59.	" " 54	"	" 4 "	"			45 00
" 60.	" " 54	"	" 5 "	"			65 00

☞ All my Vanes are of copper, and gilded with gold leaf.

EAGLE AND ARROW.

No. 45½.	14 feet, spread	....	$600 00
" 46½.	12 " "		500 00
" 47½.	10 " "		425 00
" 48.	8 " "		300 00
" 49.	7 " "		225 00
" 50.	6 " 6 inches		185 00
" 49½.	6 "		170 00
" 50½.	5 " 6 inches		150 00
" 51.	5 "		135 00
" 52.	4 "		70 00
" 52½.	3 " 6 inches		50 00
" 53.	3 "		47 00
" 54.	2 " 3 inches		31 00
" 55.	1 foot 8 "		21 00
" 56.	1 " 3 "		15 00
" 56½.	0 " 9 "		8 00

☞ All my Vanes are of copper, and gilded with gold leaf.

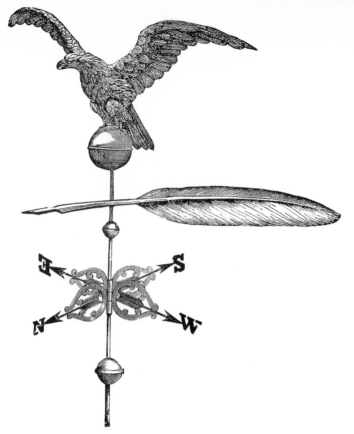

EAGLE AND PEN.

No. 320.   Eagle, 3 feet, spread, with 4 feet pen .... $ 55 00
"   321.   "   3 "   6 inches, spread, with 4 feet 6 inches pen 65 00
"   322.   "   4 "   spread, with 5 feet pen 85 00
"   323.   "   5 "   "   "   6 "   " 150 00
"   324.   "   6 "   "   "   7 "   " 190 00
"   325.   "   7 "   6 inches, spread, with 9 feet pen 250 00

This Vane was designed expressly for the "*Staatz Zeitung*" Newspaper Building.

CAST ZINC EAGLES.

For Flag Poles, Lamps, Store Signs, Monuments, Etc., are not suitable for Vanes.

No. 209.   3 inches, spread .... $ 1 25
"   210.   4   "   " 2 25
"   211.   6½   "   " 3 25
"   212.   7   "   " 4 00
"   213. 10   "   " 5 00
"   214. 13   "   " 8 00
"   215. 14   "   " 10 00
"   216. 18   "   " 15 00
"   217. 22   "   " 15 00
"   218. 30   "   " 24 00
"   219. 31   "   " 38 00
"   220. 50   "   " 50 00
"   221. 60   "   " 96 00

☞ All my Vanes are of copper, and gilded with gold leaf.

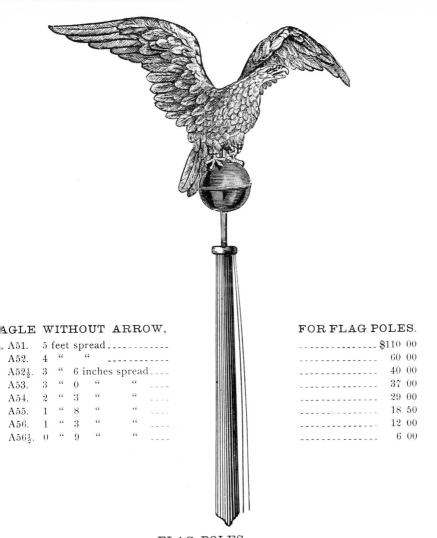

EAGLE WITHOUT ARROW,			FOR FLAG POLES.
A51.	5 feet spread _____		_____ $110 00
A52.	4 " " _____		_____ 60 00
A52½.	3 " 6 inches spread ____		_____ 40 00
A53.	3 " 0 " " ____		_____ 37 00
A54.	2 " 3 " " ____		_____ 29 00
A55.	1 " 8 " " ____		_____ 18 50
A56.	1 " 3 " " ____		_____ 12 00
A56½.	0 " 9 " " ____		_____ 6 00

FLAG POLES.

feet long, 4 inches diameter at Butt, $10 00						50 feet long, 8 inches diameter at Butt, $40 00										
" " 5 " " " " 15 00						50 " " 9 " " " " 45 00										
" " 6 " " " " 18 00						55 " " 9 " " " " 55 00										
" " 7 " " " " 23 00						60 " " 9 " " " " 70 00										
" " 8 " " " " 27 00						65 " " 10 " " " " 100 00										
" " 8 " " " " 35 00						70 " " 11 " " " " 110 00										

LIGNUMVITAE TRUCKS.

	ONE SHEAVE.	TWO SHEAVES.			ONE SHEAVE.	TWO SHEAVES.
inches diameter, each __	$1 20	$1 60	6 inches diameter, each __	$1 75		$2 50
" " " __	1 30	1 80	7 " " " __	2 25		3 00
" " " __	1 40	2 00	8 " " " __	2 50		3 50
" " " __	1 50	2 25				

☞ All my Vanes are of copper, and gilded with gold leaf.

PAWNBROKER'S BALLS AND BRACKET.

No. 569.   8 inch balls _____ per set, $11
          9   "   "   _____   "   "   18
         10   "   "   _____   "   "   23
Bracket, 3 feet projection _____ 10

PLAIN BRACKETS MADE TO ORDER.
Copyrighted 1893.

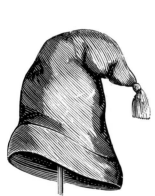

LIBERTY CAP.

No. 94.   6 inches high, $ 7 50
 " 95.   9   "   "   12 00
 " 96. 12   "   "   15 00
 " 97. 15   "   "   20 00
 " 98. 18   "   "   30 00
 " 99. 24   "   "   40 00

No. 570.
WROUGHT IRON FLAG-POLE HOLDER
FOR CORNERS OF BUILDINGS.
Estimates given upon application. Any size made to order
Copyrighted 1893.

METAL BALLS FOR FLAG POLES.

ı Stems, gilded with best gold leaf.

		ZINC.	COPPER.
. 226.	3 inches...each, $	70	$ 1 00
227.	4 " ... "	1 10	1 50
228.	5 " ... "	1 40	2 50
229.	6 " ... "	2 00	4 00
230.	7 " ... "	3 00	6 00
231.	8 " ... "	3 50	7 50
232.	9 " ... "	6 00	9 00
233.	10 " ... "	7 75	10 00
234.	12 " ... "	12 00	16 00

Not on Stems, gilded with best gold leaf for Vanes or other purposes.

				ZINC.	COPPER.
No. 235.	1 inch......each, $			25	$ 50
" 236.	2 inches... "			36	70
" 237.	2½ " ... "			46	80
" 238.	3 " ... "			60	90
" 239.	4 " ... "			96	1 40
" 240.	5 " ... "			1 25	2 25
" 241.	6 " ... "			1 60	3 50
" 242.	7 " ... "			2 60	5 50
" 243.	8 " ... "			3 00	7 00
" 244.	9 " ... "			4 50	8 00
" 245.	10 " ... "			5 00	9 00
" 246.	12 " ... "			7 50	14 00
" 247.	15 " ... "			18 00	25 00
" 248.	18 " ... "			25 00	35 00

STAR.

FLAG POLE BALLS OF BEST SEASONED WHITE WOOD.

2 inches diameter..........each, $		30
2½ " "	"	50
3 " "	"	65
4 " "	"	1 30
5 " "	"	1 80
6 " "	"	2 50
7 " "	"	3 50
8 " "	"	4 50
9 " "	"	5 50
10 " "	"	6 75

		9 in.	12 in.	15 in.	18 in.	24 in.
o. 106.	5 points,	$4 00	$5 50	$7 50	$10 00	$16 00
107.	6 "	5 00	6 50	8 50	11 00	17 00
108.	9 "	10 00	13 00	17 00	22 00	34 00
109.	10 "	12 00	15 00	19 00	25 00	37 00
110.	12 "	14 00	17 00	21 00	28 00	40 00
111.	14 "	16 00	18 00	25 00	33 00	50 00

METAL BALLS, WITH STAR TOP FINISH.

8 inch Ball, 9 inch 9 point star $14 00

9 inch Ball, 9 inch 9 point star 16 50

10 inch Ball, 10 inch 9 point star............. 20 00

METAL BALLS, WITH WOOD TOP FINISH.

GILDED WITH GOLD LEAF.

		ZINC.	COPPER.
4 inch Ball	.....$1 50		$2 00
5 " "	..... 2 00		3 00
6 " "	..... 2 75		5 00
7 " "	..... 4 00		7 00
8 " "	..... 4 75		9 25
10 " "	..... 9 00		12 25

ANGEL GABRIEL.

No. 90.   23 inches, mounted complete as shown on page 46 _ _ _ _ _ _ _ _ _ _ _ _ _ _ _ _ _ _ $ 30
 "   91.   30   "   "   "   "   "   46 _ _ _ _ _ _ _ _ _ _ _ _ _ _ _ _ _ _   40
 "   92.   36   "   "   "   "   "   46 _ _ _ _ _ _ _ _ _ _ _ _ _ _ _ _ _ _   60
 "   93.   54   "   "   "   "   "   46 _ _ _ _ _ _ _ _ _ _ _ _ _ _ _ _ _ _   100

GODDESS OF LIBERTY.

No. 87.   24 inches high, mounted complete as shown on page 46 _ _ _ _ _ _ _ _ _ _ _ _ _ _ $30 00
 "   88.   36   "   "   "   "   "   "   46 _ _ _ _ _ _ _ _ _ _ _ _ _ _   45 00

☞ All my Vanes are of copper, and gilded with gold leaf.

FIREMAN'S HAT AND TRUMPET.

No. 371. Hat, 2 feet long ; Trumpet, 2 feet 9 inches long --------------------$55 00
" 372. " 2 " 6 inches long ; Trumpet, 3 feet long --------------------- 65 00

Price include being mounted complete as shown on page 46.

HOOK AND LADDER.

No. 373. 6 feet long, mounted complete as shown on page 46----------------$ 90 00
" 374. 7 " " " " " " 46------------------- 100 00

☞ All my Vanes are of copper, and gilded with gold leaf.

STEAM FIRE ENGINE.

No. 535.   7 feet long, with horses, driver and fireman, mounted complete as shown
on page 46 _____$275 (

ANY SIZE MADE TO ORDER.

Copyrighted, 1893.

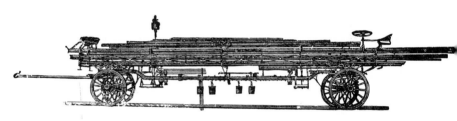

HOOK AND LADDER.

No. 309.   5 feet long, mounted complete as shown on page 46_____$110 00
"   310.   6 "   "   "   "   "   "   46_____ 130 00

MADE WITH HORSES AND MEN TO ORDER.

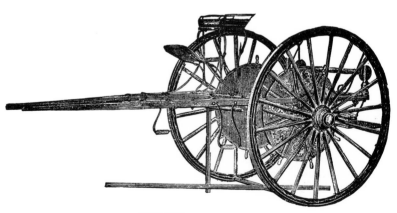

HORSE CARRIAGE.

No. 315.   3 feet 6 inches long, mounted complete as shown on page 46_____$ 85 00
"   316.   4 " 6 "   "   "   "   "   "   46_____ 100 00

MADE WITH HORSES AND DRIVER TO ORDER.

☞ All my Vanes are of copper, and gilded with gold leaf.

FIREMAN.

No. 534. ¾ Full-bodied, 30 inches high, with 5 feet arrow, mounted complete as shown on page 46 _____$140 00

Copyrighted 1893.

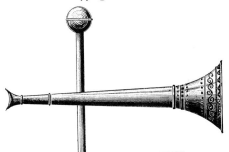

FIREMAN'S TRUMPET.

No. 536. 2 feet 9 inches long, mounted complete as shown on page 46 _____$38 00

Copyrighted 1893.

LOCOMOTIVE AND TENDER.

No. 537. 72 inches long, mounted complete as shown on page 46 _____$250 00

Copyrighted 1893.

☞ All my Vanes are of copper, and gilded with gold leaf.

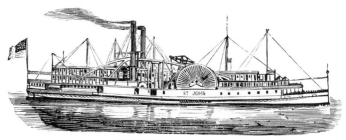

RIVER STEAMER.

No. 42.   48 inches long, mounted complete as shown on page 56 _____ $125 00

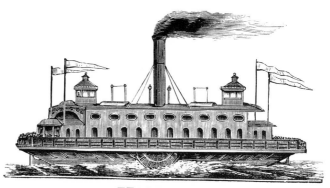

FERRY BOAT.

No. 41.   36 inches long, mounted complete as shown on page 56 _____ $150 00

OCEAN STEAMER.

No. 43.   54 inches long, mounted complete as shown on page 56 _____ $110 00

☞ All my Vanes are of copper, and gilded with gold leaf.

HORSE CAR.

No. 71. 66 inches long, perfect model, with pair of horses attached, and driver
and conductor, mounted complete as shown on page 56 .... $200 00

☞ TROLLEY CAR, ANY SIZE TO ORDER.

CANNON.

No. 104. 20 inches long, mounted complete as shown on page 56 .... $30 00
" 105. 30 " " " " " " 56 .... 45 00

GUN AND CAP.

No. 311. 5 feet long, mounted complete as shown on page 56 .... $55 00
" 312. 6 " " " " " " 56 .... 65 00

☞ All my Vanes are of copper, and gilded with gold leaf.

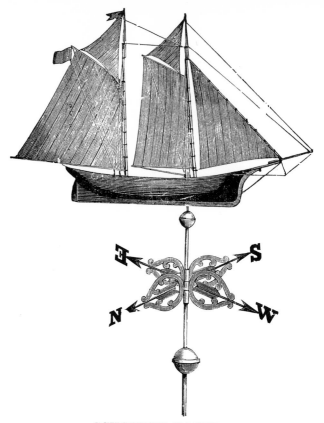

SCHOONER YACHT.

No. 336. 3 feet long_____$65 00
 "   337. 3 "   6 inches long_____ 75 00

ANY SIZE MADE TO ORDER.

SLOOP.

No. 205. 3 feet long, mounted complete as shown above_____$55 00
 "   206. 4 "   "   "   "   "   "   _____ 65 00

☞ All my Vanes are of copper, and gilded with gold leaf.

SHIP.

No. 44.   34 inches long, mounted complete as shown on page 56............$ 75 00
" 45.   48   "   "   "   "   "   " 56............... 100 00

PEACOCK.

No. 112.   36 inches long, mounted complete as shown on page 56...........$50 00
" 113.   42   "   "   "   "   "   " 56............... 70 00

ANY SIZE MADE TO ORDER.

PLOUGH.

No. 46.   36 inches long, mounted complete as shown on page 56............$24 00
" 47.   54   "   "   "   "   "   " 56............... 36 00

ANY SIZE MADE TO ORDER.

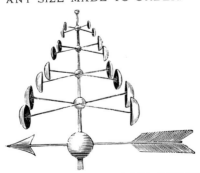

CUPS AND BALLS, WITH ARROW.

No. 122.   With 2 feet arrow, mounted complete as shown on page 56..........$18 00
" 123.   " 2 " 6 inches,   "   "   "   " 56.......... 25 00
" 124.   " 3 " mounted complete as shown on page 56................ 33 00

☞ All my Vanes are of copper, and gilded with gold leaf.

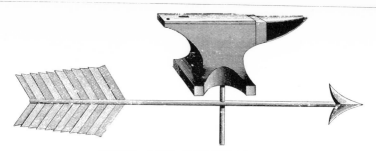

ANVIL AND ARROW VANE.

No. 529.   6 feet arrow, with 20 inches anvil, mounted complete as shown on
page 56 --$120 00

ANY SIZE MADE TO ORDER.
Copyrighted 1893.

ARROW AND SHOE VANE.

No. 529½.   6 feet arrow, with 2 feet shoe, mounted complete as shown on page
56 --$120 00

ANY SIZE MADE TO ORDER.
Copyrighted 1893.

BICYCLE AND ARROW VANE.

No. 530.   6 feet arrow, with 30 inches bicycle and rider, mounted complete as
shown on page 56--$175 00

Copyrighted, 1893.

☞ All my Vanes are of copper, and gilded with gold leaf.

MERCURY.

No. 533.   ¾ Full-bodied, 3 feet high, with 4 feet 6 inches arrow, mounted complete as shown on page 56 _$125 00

Copyrighted 1893.

LIBERTY ENLIGHTENING THE WORLD.

No. 532.   ¾ Full-bodied, 33 inches high, with 4 feet arrow, mounted complete as shown on page 56 _$85 00

Copyrighted 1893.

☞ All my Vanes are of copper, and gilded with gold leaf.

OSTRICH.

No. 527.   ¾ Full-bodied, 3 feet 6 inches high, mounted complete as shown on page
. 61 --$65 00

Copyrighted 1893.

INDIAN CHIEF.

No. 528.   ¾ Full-bodied, Indian, 3 feet 6 inches high ; arrow, 5 feet 6 inches long,
mounted complete as shown on page 61--$70 00

Copyrighted 1893.

☞ All my Vanes are of copper, and gilded with gold leaf.

GAMBRINUS.

No. 356½. 3 feet 9 inches high_____$150 00
" 357½. 5 " high_____ 200 00

☞ All my Vanes are of copper, and gilded with gold leaf.

DRAGON.

No. 368. 2 feet 2 inches long, lower ornaments of iron, 4 sided - - - - - - - - - - - $75 00

☞ All my Vanes are of copper, and gilded with gold leaf.

TIFFANY SCROLL.

No. 256. 6 feet long _____$60 00
"   257. 7½ "   "   _____   80 00

All my Vanes are of copper, and gilded with gold leaf.

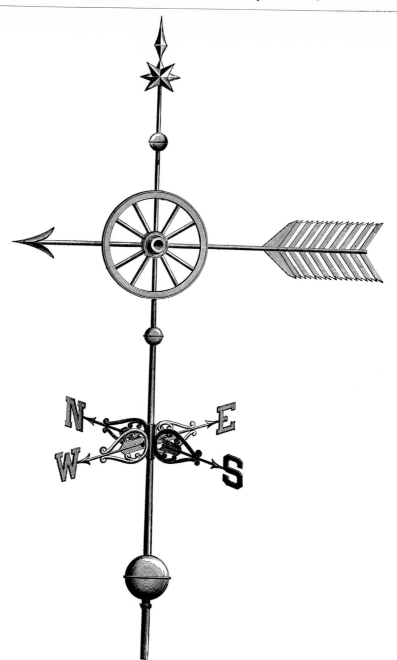

WAGON WHEEL AND ARROW VANE.

No. 538.   7 feet long _____$100 00

ANY SIZE MADE TO ORDER.

Copyrighted 1893.

☞ All my Vanes are of copper, and gilded with gold leaf.

ARROW, RING AND STAR VANE.

No. 296. 6 feet long --$ 80 00
" 297. 7 "   " -- 90 00
" 298. 8 "   " -- 125 00

☞ All my Vanes are of copper, and gilded with gold leaf.

SCROLL AND ARROW SIGN VANE.

No. 284.   5 feet long .... $ 80 00
"   285.   6   "   " 100 00
"   286.   7   "   6 inches long 130 00

☞ All my Vanes are of copper, and gilded with gold leaf.

ARROW AND STAR SIGN VANE.

No. 252. 5 feet long, mounted complete as shown on page 66_____$100 00
"   252½. 6 "   "   "   "   "   "   66_____ 125 00

☞ All my Vanes are of copper, and gilded with gold leaf.

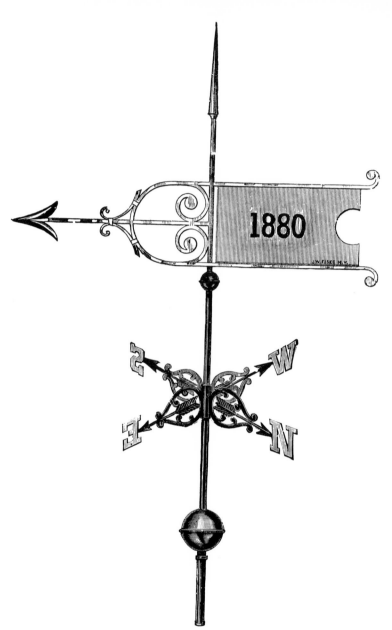

BANNERET.

No. 294.   4 feet long _____$65 00
 "   295.   4 "   " 6 inches long _____ 70 00

Any number, monogram, or initial, cut in panel without extra charge.

☞ All my Vanes are of copper, and gilded with gold leaf.

SCROLL AND LOCOMOTIVE.

No. 287.   6 feet long--$140 00

This Vane was designed expressly for the New York Elevated Railroad, and put upon their station at South Ferry.

FANCY SCROLL.

No. 356.   6 feet long ---$72 00
"   357.   7 "   "   --- 85 00

☞ All my Vanes are of copper, and gilded with gold leaf.

FANCY SCROLL.

No. 358. 5 feet long _____$50 00
  "   359. 6   "   "   _____ 70 00
  "   360. 7   "   "   _____ 80 00

☞ All my Vanes are of copper, and gilded with gold leaf.

GRECIAN SCROLL.

No. 251.   4 feet long, points of compass, of copper and gilded----------------$80 00

☞ All my Vanes are of copper, and gilded with gold leaf.

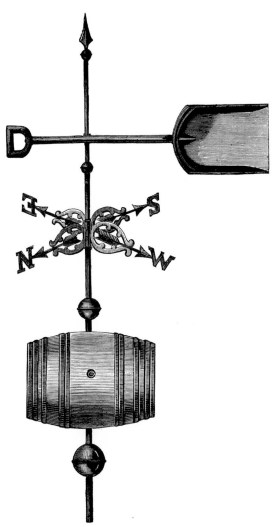

MALT SHOVEL AND BARREL.

FURNISHED EITHER SEPARATELY OR TOGETHER.

ɔ. 250.	Shovel, 5 feet long, barrel raised 6 inches				$80 00
A250.	" 5 " " without barrel				60 00
B250.	" 6 " " " "				75 00
C250.	" 7 " " " "				90 00

ANY SIZE SHOVEL MADE TO ORDER WITH BARREL.

☞ All my Vanes are of copper, and gilded with gold leaf.

BANNERET.

No. 404.   3 feet long..$200

☞ All my Vanes are of copper, and gilded with gold leaf.

DOLPHIN BANNERET.

No. 401.   Banneret, 2 feet 6 inches long _$90 00
☞ All my Vanes are of copper, and gilded with gold leaf.

ROOSTER AND SCROLL BANNERET.

No. 400.   Vane, 2 feet 6 inches long; Finial of iron------------------$170 00

☞ All my Vanes are of copper, and gilded with gold leaf.

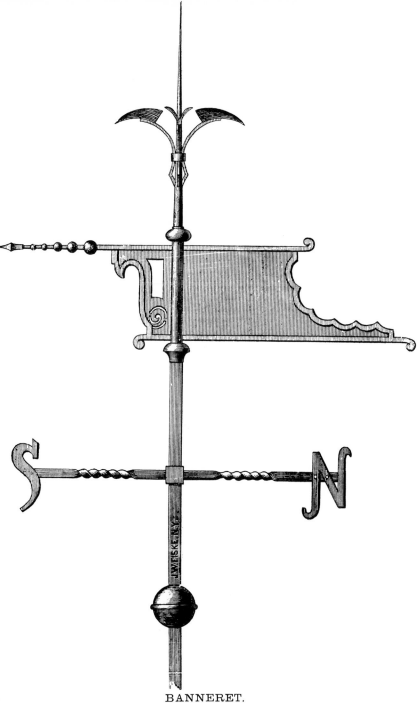

BANNERET.

o. 402.   4 feet 4 inches long, mounted as shown above_____$100 00
mounted on Points of Compass as shown on page 78 _____ _____ 90 00
☞ All my Vanes are of copper, and gilded with gold leaf.

BANNERET.

No. 403. 3 feet 6 inches long--$75

☞ All my Vanes are of copper, and gilded with gold leaf.

BANNERET.

No. 405.   Banneret, 3 feet 6 inches long ----------------------------------$135 00

☞ All my Vanes are of copper, and gilded with gold leaf.

BANNERETS AND FINIALS.

No. 369. Banneret, 3 feet 6 inches long,   No. 370. Banneret, 2 feet 6 inches long,
   without galvanized iron base....$125 00   without galvanized iron base....$150 00
        ☞ Galvanized iron or copper bases for Finials and Vanes made to order.

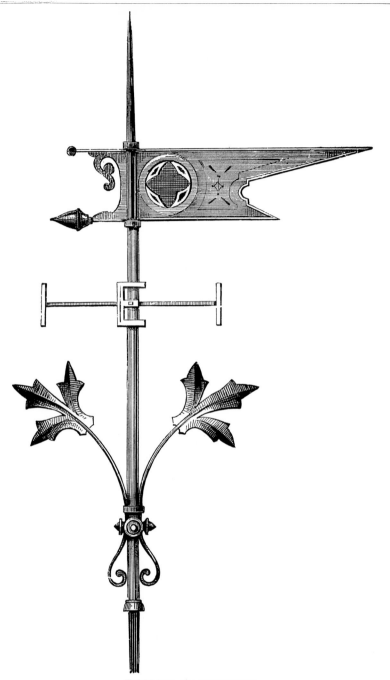

ROMAN BANNERET.

No 263.   3 feet long, lower ornaments of iron, 4 sided........................$70 00
"   264.   3 "   6 inches long, lower ornaments of iron, 4 sided................. 85 00

☞ All my Vanes are of copper, and gilded with gold leaf.

STAR AND CRESCENT BANNERET.

No 365   3 feet long _$55 00

☞ All my Vanes are of copper, and gilded with gold leaf.

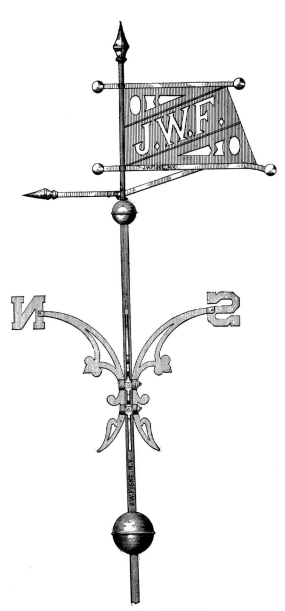

INITIAL BANNERET.

No. 366.   3 feet long ---$50 00

Any initials cut in panel without extra charge.

☞ All my Vanes are of copper, and gilded with gold leaf.

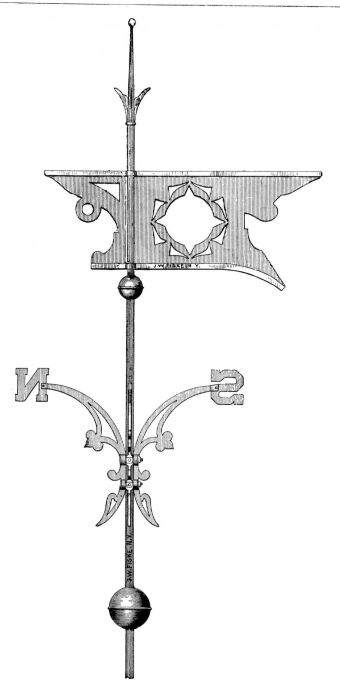

BANNERET.

No. 364.   3 feet long _____ $50 00

☞ All my Vanes are of copper, and gilded with gold leaf.

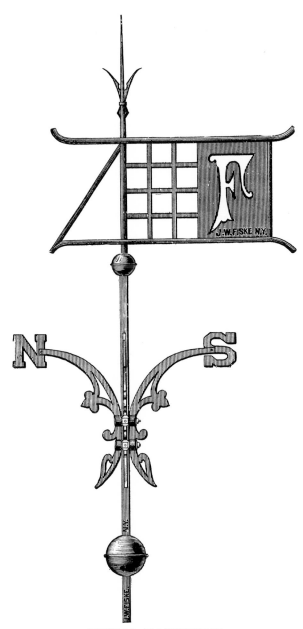

INITIAL BANNERET.

No. 375. 2 feet 6 inches long $35 00
" 376. 3 " long 40 00

Any initial cut in panel without extra charge.

☞ All my Vanes are of copper, and gilded with gold leaf.

BANNERET.

No. 377.   3 feet long --$55 00

☞ All my Vanes are of copper, and gilded with gold leaf.

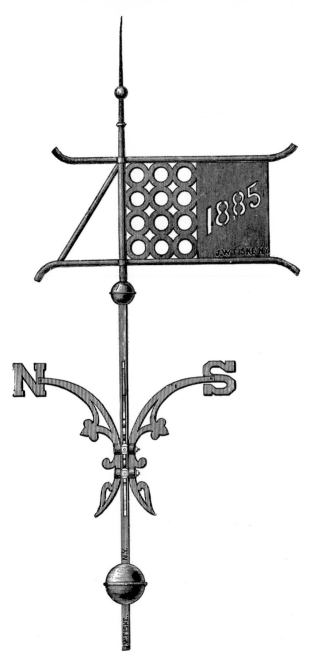

INITIAL BANNERET.

☞ All my Vanes are of copper, and gilded with gold leaf.

BANNERET.

No. 380.   3 feet long _____$75 0

"   381.   3   "   6 inches long _____ 85 0

☞ All my Vanes are of copper, and gilded with gold leaf.

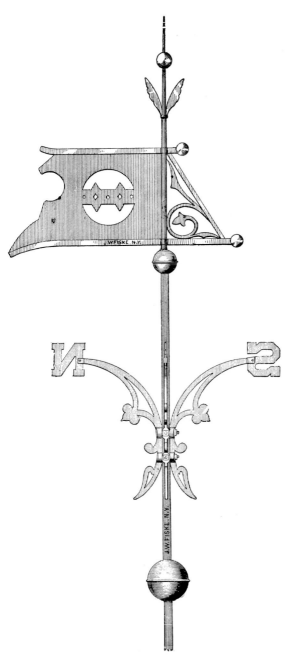

BANNERET.

☞ All my Vanes are of copper, and gilded with gold leaf.

ENGLISH BANNERET.

No. 259.   Banneret, 3 feet long, scroll copper and gilded_____ _____$100 (

☞ All my Vanes are of copper, and gilded with gold leaf.

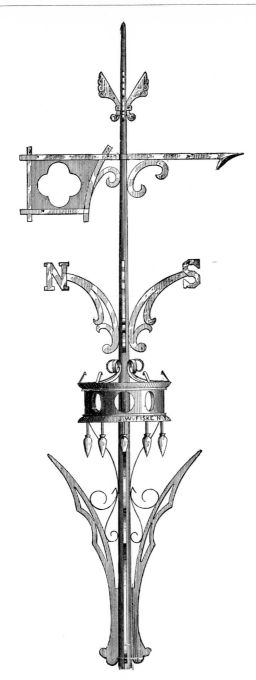

BANNERET AND CROWN FINIAL.

No. 361.   Banneret, 4 feet long, complete as shown above_____$130 00

☞ Gilded and decorated in any color.

ANY SIZE MADE TO ORDER.

GRECIAN BANNERET.

No. 261.   3½ feet, 4 sided, as shown above, with scroll $70 00
"   261¼.   3½   "   mounted as shown on page 89, without scroll................ 65 00
"   262.   4½   "   4 sided, as shown above, with scroll...................... 80 00
"   262¼.   4½   "   mounted as shown on page 89, without scroll.............. 75 00

Banneret and Scroll made of copper, and gilded.

☞ All my Vanes are of copper, and gilded with gold leaf.

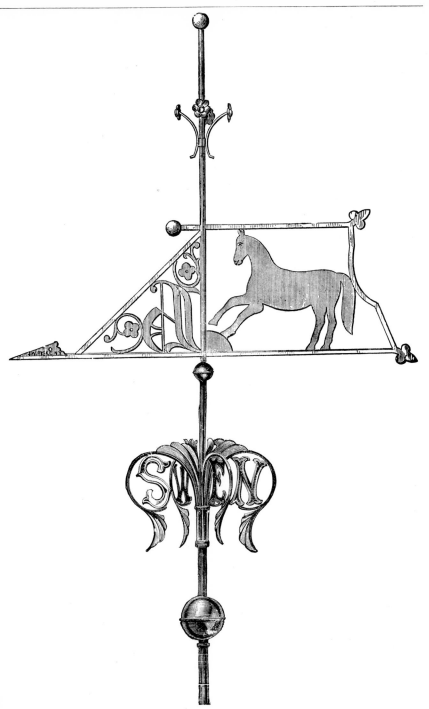

BANNERET.

No. 308.   4 feet long, points of compass of copper and gilded $85 00
"   308½. 4   "   "   mounted as shown on page 89 .... 75 00

☞ All my Vanes are of copper, and gilded with gold leaf.

BANNERET.

No. 556.   3 feet long _____$120 00

Banneret of copper gilded, scroll work and spire of iron, decorated in gold and colors.
Copyrighted, 1893.

☞ All my Vanes are of copper, and gilded with gold leaf.

BANNERET.

No. 558. 2 feet 9 inches long- -$100 00

Banneret of copper gilded, scroll work and spire of iron, decorated in gold and colors.

Copyrighted 1893.

☞ All my Vanes are of copper, and gilded with gold leaf.

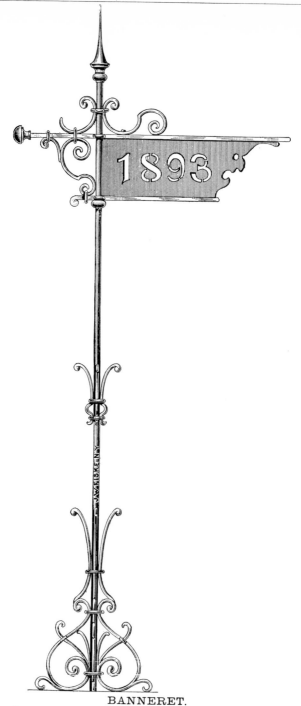

BANNERET.

No. 559.   3 feet long_____$120 00

Banneret of copper gilded, scroll work of iron, decorated in gold and colors.

Copyrighted 1893.

☞ All my Vanes are of copper, and gilded with gold leaf

BANNERET.

No. 557. 3 feet long --$120 00

Banneret of copper gilded, scroll work and spire of iron, decorated in gold and colors
Copyrighted 1893.

☞ All my Vanes are of copper, and gilded with gold leaf.

BANNERET.

No. 562. 2 feet 6 inches long ____ $100 00

BANNERET.

No. 563. 3 feet long _____ $140 00

Bannerets of copper gilded, scroll work of iron, decorated in gold and colors.
Price does not include galvanized iron or copper caps, which are made to order any size.

BANNERET.
No. 564. 2 feet 6 inches long____$100 00

BANNERET.
No. 565. 2 feet 6 inches long_____$80 00

Bannerets of copper gilded, scroll work of iron, decorated in gold and colors.
Price does not include galvanized iron or copper caps, which are made to order any size.
Copyrighted, 1893.

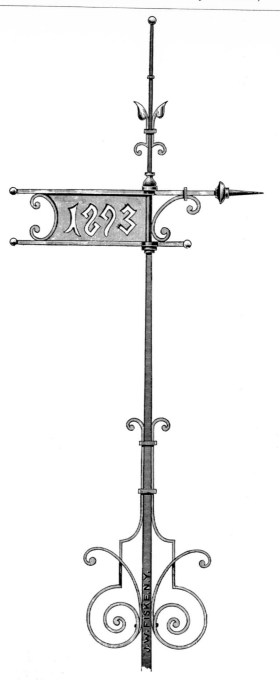

BANNERET.

No. 560.   3 feet long--$115 00

Banneret of copper gilded, scroll work of iron, decorated in gold and colors.

Copyrighted 1893.

BANNERET. ALL COPPER.

No. 490.   3 feet long, gilded, upright rod painted _____ $100 00

Copyrighted 1893.

☞ All my Vanes are of copper, and gilded with gold leaf.

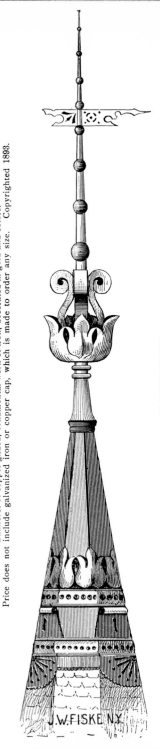

BANNERET.

No. 502.   3 feet 6 inches long ------------------------------$175 00
    Banneret of copper gilded, ornamental work of iron, decorated in gold and colors.
Price does not include galvanized iron or copper cap, which is made to order any size.   Copyrighted 1893.

BANNERET.

No. 488.   3 feet 6 inches long ------------------------------$90 00

BANNERET.

No. 504. 2 feet 6 inches long --------------------- $135 00

Banneret of copper gilded, ornamental work of iron, decorated in gold and colors.

Price does not include galvanized iron or copper cap, which is made to order any size.

Copyrighted 1893.

BANNERET AND FINIAL.

No. 363.   2 feet 9 inches long, as shown above _____$44

Banneret of copper and gilded, finial of iron, decorated in gold and colors.

☞ All my Vanes are of copper, and gilded with gold leaf.

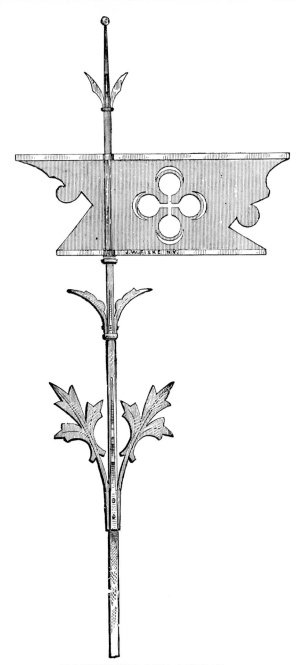

BANNERET AND FINIAL.

o 362.   3 feet long, as shown above..$46 00

Banneret of copper and gilded, finial of iron, decorated in gold and colors.

☞ All my Vanes are of copper, and gilded with gold leaf.

BANNERET.

No. 561.   2 feet 6 inches long _____$80 00

Banneret of copper, ornamental work of galvanized iron, decorated in gold and colors.

Copyrighted 1893.

BANNERET.

BANNERET.

No. 566. 2 feet 6 inches long____$135 00   No. 487. 1 foot 6 inches long_____$25 00

Bannerets of copper, scroll work of iron, decorated in gold and colors.

Price does not include galvanized iron or copper caps, which are made to order any size.

PRICE GIVEN UPON APPLICATION.

Copyrighted 1893.

BANNERET.   **BANNERET.**

No. 501.   2 feet 6 inches long____$70 00   No. 498.   2 feet 6 inches long_ ____$70 00

Bannerets and points of compass of copper gilded, spire and ornaments of iron,

decorated in gold and colors.

Copyrighted 1893.

BANNERET.

No. 500. 2 feet 6 inches long_____$75 00

Banneret and points of compass of copper gilded, ornamental work of iron, decorated in gold and colors.

Copyrighted 1893.

BANNERET.

No. 489. 2 feet 6 inches long_____$70 00

Banneret and points of compass of copper gilded, ball and base of iron, decorated in gold and colors.

Copyrighted 1893.

J.W.FISKE,N.Y.

J.W.FISKE,

BANNERET.

No. 495. 1 foot 6 inches
long ----------- $20 00
Banneret of copper gilded,
ornamental work of iron,
decorated in gold
and colors.
Price does not include cap
or base.
Copyrighted 1893.

BANNERET.

No. 568. 1 foot 6 inches
long ----------- $30 00
Banneret of copper gilded,
ornamental work of iron,
decorated in gold
and colors.
Copyrighted 1893.

BANNERET.

No. 497. 2 feet 6 inches
long ----------- $50 00
Banneret of copper gilded,
ornamental work of iron,
decorated in gold
and colors.
Copyrighted 1893.

BANNERET.

No. 499. 1 foot 3 inches
long......................$60 00
Banneret of copper gilded,
ornamental work of iron,
decorated in gold
and colors.
Copyrighted 1893.

BANNERET.

No. 567. 2 feet long, $60 00
Banneret of copper gilded,
ornamental work of iron,
decorated in gold
and colors.
Copyrighted 1893.

BANNERET.

No. 496. 2 feet long, $45 00
Banneret of copper gilded,
scroll work of iron,
decorated in gold
and colors.
Copyrighted 1893.

ENGLISH BANNERET.	FISH VANE.
No. 493. 3 feet long_____$125 00	No. 494. 2 feet long_____$65 00

ENGLISH BANNERET.

No. 493.   3 feet long_____$125 00

Banneret and points of compass of copper
gilded, cap of copper or galvanized iron,
made to order any size, extra.

Price upon application.

Copyrighted 1893.

FISH VANE.

No. 494.   2 feet long_____$65 00

Fish of copper gilded, iron work
decorated in gold and colors.

Copyrighted 1893.

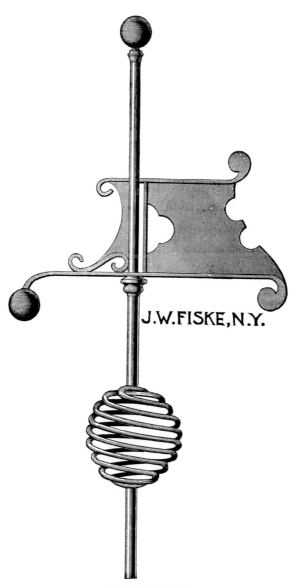

BANNERET.

No. 492.   3 feet long.. $80 00

Banneret of copper, ornamental work of iron, decorated in gold and colors.

Copyrighted 1893.

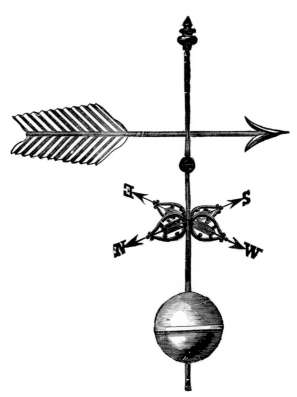

ARROW.

No. 134.	1 foot long				$	4 00
" 133.	1 "	3 inches long				5 00
" 132.	1 "	6 "	"			6 00
" 131.	2 feet long					8 00
" 130.	2 "	6 inches long				10 00
" 129.	3 "	long				15 00
" 128.	3 "	6 inches long				18 00
" 127.	4 "	long				20 00
" 126.	5 "	"				30 00
" 125.	6 "	"				50 00
" 306.	7 "	"				70 00
" 307.	8 "	"				100 00

☞ All my Vanes are of copper, and gilded with gold leaf

CHURCH OR SCROLL VANE.

No. 135.	Church Vane,	12 feet long	$125 00
" 136.	" "	10 " "	100 00
" 137.	" "	8 " "	90 00
" 138.	" "	7 " "	80 00
" 139.	" "	6 " "	65 00
" 140.	" "	5½ " "	45 00
" 141	" "	5 " "	35 00
" 142.	" "	4½ " "	25 00
" 143.	" "	4 " "	23 00
" 144.	Small Scroll,	4 " "	20 00
" 145.	" "	3½ " "	18 00
" 146.	" "	3 " "	15 00
" 147.	" "	2½ " "	12 00
" 148.	" "	24 inches long	10 00
" 149.	" "	18 " "	8 00
" 150.	" "	15 " "	6 00
" 151.	" "	12 " "	5 00
" 152.	" "	8 " "	4 00

☞ All my Vanes are of copper, and gilded with gold leaf.

ROMAN SCROLL.

No. 253. 3 feet long --$19 00
"   254. 4   "   " -- 25 00
"   255. 5   "   " -- 40 00

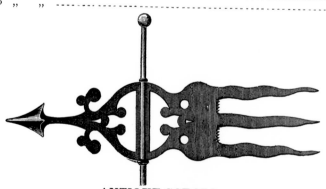

ANTIQUE SCROLL.

No. 540. 4 feet long, mounted complete as shown above_____$60 00
Copyrighted 1893.
☞ All my Vanes are of copper, and gilded with gold leaf.

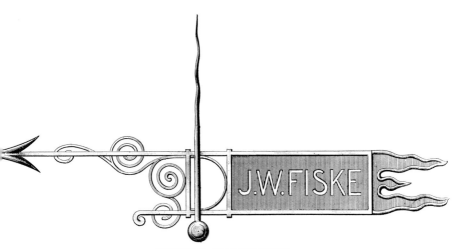

SCROLL BANNERET.

o. 545.   4 feet long, mounted complete as shown on page 116 ---------------$90 00

ANY SIZE MADE TO ORDER.

Copyrighted 1893.

WAGON AND SCROLL BANNERET.

o. 546.   4 feet 6 inches long, mounted complete as shown on page 116---------$65 00

ANY SIZE MADE TO ORDER.

Copyrighted 1893.

☞ All my Vanes are of copper, and gilded with gold leaf.

NAME BANNERET.

No. 547.	6 feet long, mounted complete as shown on page 116	116	$125 0
" 548.	7 " " " " " "	116	150 0
" 549.	8 " " " " " "	116	180 0

ANY SIZE MADE TO ORDER.

Copyrighted 1893.

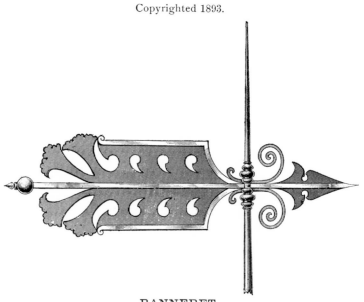

BANNERET.

No. 550.   3 feet 6 inches long, mounted complete as shown on page 116 _____$75 0

ANY SIZE MADE TO ORDER.

Copyrighted, 1893.

☞ All my Vanes are of copper, and gilded with gold leaf.

ANTIQUE SLOOP.

No. 541.   2 feet 6 inches long, mounted complete as shown on page 116 _____ _____$40 00

Copyrighted 1893.

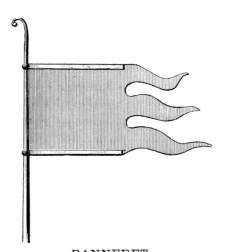

BANNERET.

No. 542.   2 feet long, mounted complete as shown on page 116 ___ ____ _____$25 00

Copyrighted 1893.

☞ All my Vanes are of copper, and gilded with gold leaf.

BANNERET.

No. 543.   1 foot 9 inches long, mounted complete as shown on page 122 _ _ _ _ _ _ _$33 00

ANY SIZE MADE TO ORDER.

Copyrighted 1893.

BANNERET.

No. 544.   2 feet 6 inches long, mounted complete as shown on page 122 _ _ _ _ _ _ _ _$40 00

ANY SIZE MADE TO ORDER.

Copyrighted 1893.

All my Vanes are of copper, and gilded with gold leaf.

SCROLL AND ARROW VANE.

No. 551. 5 feet long, mounted complete as shown on page 122 _____ $70 00
" 552. 6 " " " " " " 122 _____ 80 00
" 553. 7 " " " " " " 122 _____ 95 00

ANY SIZE MADE TO ORDER.
Copyrighted 1893.

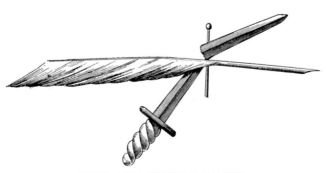

PEN AND SWORD VANE.

No. 554. 3 feet 6 inches long, mounted complete as shown on page 122 _____ $50 00
" 555. 4 " 6 " " " " " " 122 _____ 65 00

ANY SIZE MADE TO ORDER.
Copyrighted 1893.

☞ All my Vanes are of copper, and gilded with gold leaf.

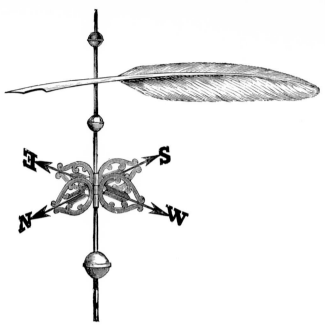

PEN.

No. 117. 2 feet long _____$ 9 00
"   118. 3 "   "   _____ 18 00
"   119. 4 "   "   _____ 25 00
"   120. 5 "   "   _____ 40 00
"   121. 6 "   "   _____ 55 00

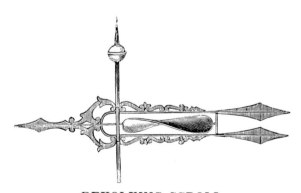

REVOLVING SCROLL.

No. 85.   4 feet 2 inches long, mounted complete as shown above _____$30 00
"   85½. 5 " long, mounted complete as shown above_____ 40 00
"   86.   6 "   "   "   "   "   "   _____ 70 00

Mica can be put on the revolvers if desired, so that it will sparkle while revolving.

☞ All my Vanes are of copper, and gilded with gold leaf.

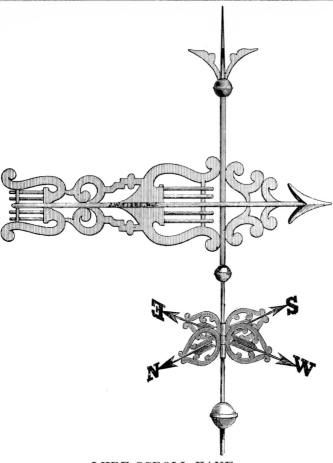

LYRE SCROLL VANE.

o. 352.   4 feet long _____$38 00
" 353.   5   "   "   _____ 48 00

REVOLVING SCROLL.

o. 80.   3 feet 6 inches long, mounted complete as shown above _____ _____$ 36 00
" 81.   4 " 8   "   "   "   "   "   "   _____ 45 00
" 82.   6 " long, mounted complete as shown above   _____ 70 00
" 83.   8 "   "   "   "   "   "   "   _____ 100 00
" 84.   10 "   "   "   "   "   "   "   _____ 150 00

☞ All my Vanes are of copper, and gilded with gold leaf.

CHURCH SCROLL.

No. 157.   6 feet long, mounted complete as shown on page 122 _____ $100
" 158.   7 "   "   "   "   "   122 _____ 130
" 158½. 8 "   "   "   "   "   122 _____ 140

INDEX SCROLL.

No. 153.   3 feet long, mounted complete as shown on page 122 _____ $18
" 154.   3 "   6 inches long, mounted complete as shown on page 122 _____ 22
" 155.   4 "   long, mounted complete as shown on page 122 _____ 25
" 156.   5 "   "   "   "   "   122 _____ 55

☞ All my Vanes are of copper, and gilded with gold leaf.

LYRE VANE.

No. 354.   3 feet 6 inches long, mounted complete as shown on page 122........$60 00

ANY SIZE MADE TO ORDER.

BANNERET.

No. 382.   2 feet long, without galvanized iron cap-----------------------------$30 00

Galvanized iron or copper bases for Finials or Vanes made to order.

☞ All my Vanes are of copper, and gilded with gold leaf.

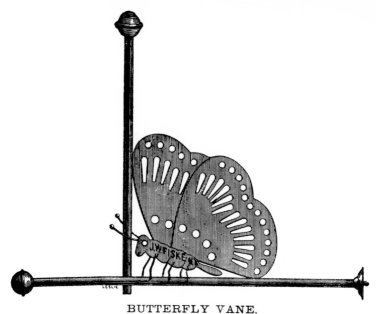

BUTTERFLY VANE.

No. 383.   2 feet 6 inches long, mounted complete as shown on page 127 _____ $18 00

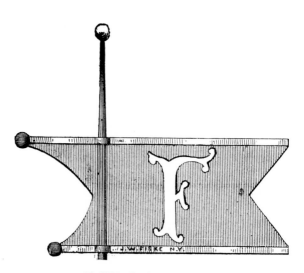

INITIAL BANNERET.

No. 355.   2 feet 6 inches long, mounted complete as shown on page 127 _____ $30 00

☞ All my Vanes are of copper, and gilded with gold leaf.

BANNERET.

o. 292.   3 feet long --$50 00

SCROLL AND ARROW.

o. 301.   5 feet long, mounted complete as shown above------------------$40 00
' 302.   6 "   "   "   "   "   " ------------------------ 58 00

☞ All my Vanes are of copper, and gilded with gold leaf.

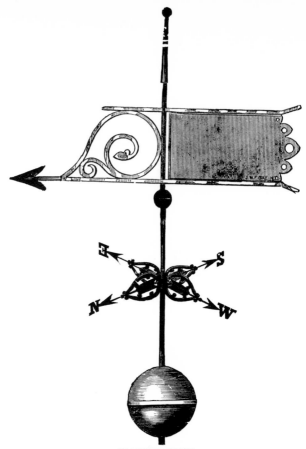

BANNERET.

No. 288.   3 feet 6 inches long _$50 00
"   289.   4 "   long _ 60 00

Any number, monogram, or initial cut in panel without extra charge.

FRENCH SCROLL.

No. 290.   3 feet long, mounted complete as shown above _ _ _ _ _ _ _ _ _ _ _ _ _ _ _ _ _ _ _ _$40 00
"   291.   4 "   "   "   "   "   " _ _ _ _ _ _ _ _ _ _ _ _ _ 45 00

INITIAL BANNERET.

No. 384. 3 feet long --$40 00
" 385. 3 " 6 inches long -- 50 00

BANNERET.

No. 386. 1 foot 6 inches long, mounted complete as shown above ------------$28 00
" 387. 2 feet long, mounted complete as shown above---------------------- 32 00

☞ All my Vanes are of copper, and gilded with gold leaf.

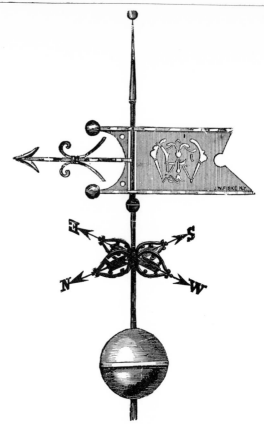

INITIAL BANNERET.

No. 299.   3 feet long _____$50 00
" 300.   3 " 6 inches long _____ 58 00
Any monogram or initial cut in panel without extra charge.

SCROLL AND LOCOMOTIVE.

No. 293.   4 feet 6 inches long, mounted complete as shown above_____$60 00
" 293½.   5 " long, mounted complete as shown above_____ 70 00
☞ All my Vanes are of copper, and gilded with gold leaf.

BANNERET.

No. 391. 2 feet 6 inches long _____$40 00
"   392. 3 " long _____ 45 00

BANNERET.

No. 397. 2 feet long, mounted complete as shown above_____$25 00
"   398. 2 " 6 inches long, mounted complete as shown above_____ 32 00

☞ All my Vanes are of copper, and gilded with gold leaf

BANNERET.

No. 388.   2 feet 6 inches long $25 00
"   389.   3   "   long 35 00

BANNERET.

No. 390.   3 feet long, mounted complete as shown above $50 00

INITIAL BANNERET.

No. 303.   3 feet long _____$45 00
Any number, monogram, or initial, cut in panel without extra charge.

SCROLL AND ARROW.

No. 304.   4 feet long, mounted complete as shown above_____ _____$35 00
"   305.   5 "   "   "   "   "   "   _____ _____ 45 00

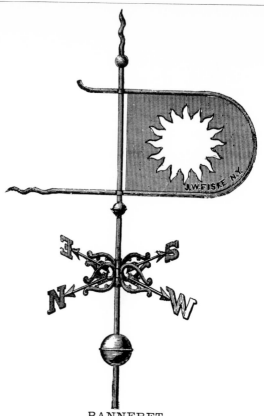

BANNERET.

No. 395.   2 feet 6 inches long _____$30 0
"   396.   3 " long _____ 40 0

INITIAL BANNERET.

No. 393.   2 feet 6 inches long. mounted complete as shown above_____ _____$32 0
"   394.   3 " 6   "   "   "   "   "   "   _____ 42 0

ENGLISH BANNERET.

No. 165. 3 feet 6 inches long, mounted complete as shown on page 134_____$50 00

ENGLISH BANNERET.

No. 180. 2 feet long, mounted complete as shown on page 134_____$25 00

ENGLISH BANNERET.

No. 160.   3 feet long, mounted complete as shown on page 134 _____ _____$45 0

ENGLISH BANNERET.

No. 170.   2 feet 6 inches long, mounted complete as shown on page 134_____$30 00

☞ All my Vanes are of copper, and gilded with gold leaf.

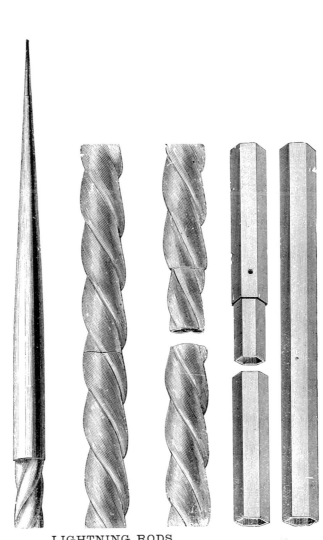

LIGHTNING RODS.

7 Strand Solid Copper Cable Rod. Price, per foot, including Points and Staples, 40c.

Polished Point for Copper Cable Rod. Each, $2.00

New Patent Copper Rod, Cable Shape, and is very easily put together. Price, per foot, including Points, Tees and connections, $\frac{9}{16}$, 28c.; $\frac{5}{8}$, 30c.

Solid Copper Hexagon Tube Rod. Price, per foot, including Points, Tees and connections, $\frac{9}{16}$, 28c.; $\frac{5}{8}$, 30c.

Special prices and estimates given for large quantities.

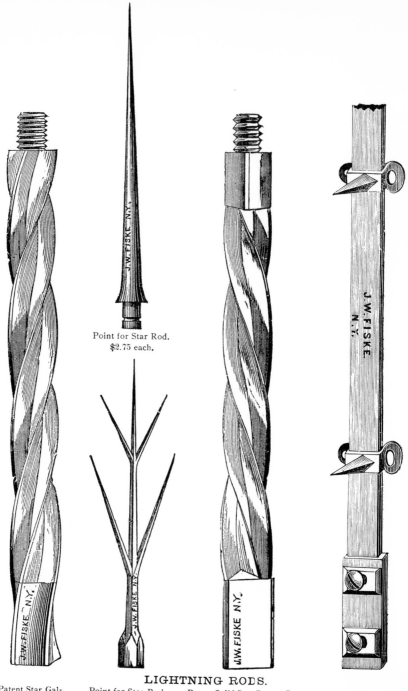

Point for Star Rod.
$2.75 each.

LIGHTNING RODS.

Patent Star Galvanized Rod.
Price, per foot, including Points and connections,
$\frac{5}{8}$, 22c.; $\frac{3}{4}$, 30c.

Point for Star Rod.
$2.75 each.

Patent Solid Star Copper Rod.
Price, per foot, including Points and connections,
$\frac{5}{8}$, 35c.
Star Rod, copper covered, per foot, $\frac{5}{8}$, 30c.

$\frac{3}{8}$ Square Galvanized Iron Rod.
Price, per foot, including Points and connections, 20c.

Special prices and estimates given for large quantities.

In addition to **COPPER WEATHER VANES**, I manufacture the largest line of

Iron, Brass and Bronze Stable Fixtures in the United States,

Also, Galvanized Iron and Copper Caps for Towers, etc.

Fig. 11½.

[M]ANGER WITH FOOD GUARDS IN CORNER.

inches long on sides, 12 inches [d]eep_____$3 00

Copyrighted 1893.
GALVANIZED IRON AND COPPER CAPS.
Any size made to order.
Either round, square or octagon.

Fig. F.

MANGER WITH FOOD GUARDS.

16 inches long on sides, 9½ inches deep_____$2 25

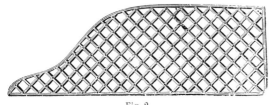

Fig. 2.

STALL GUARD.

5 feet long, 2 feet high_____each $4 00	6 feet 6 inches long, 2 feet 4 inches high__each $5 50
5 " 0 inches long, 2 feet 4 inches high__ " 4 50	7 " 0 " " 2 " 4 " " __ " 6 00
5 " 6 " " 2 " 4 " " __ " 4 75	7 " 6 " " 2 " 4 " " __ " 6 50
6 " 0 " " 2 " 4 " " __ " 5 00	8 " 0 " " 2 " 4 " " __ " 7 00

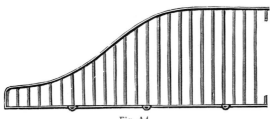

Fig. A4.

STALL GUARD.

5 feet long, 2 feet 4 inches high _____each $7 00	7 feet 0 inches long, 2 feet 4 inches high, each $10 00
5 " 6 inches long, 2 feet 4 inches high__ " 7 75	7 " 6 " " 2 " 4 " " " 11 00
6 " 0 " " 2 " 4 " " __ " 8 50	8 " 0 " " 2 " 4 " " " 12 00
6 " 6 " " 2 " 4 " " __ " 9 50	8 " 6 " " 2 " 4 " " " 13 00

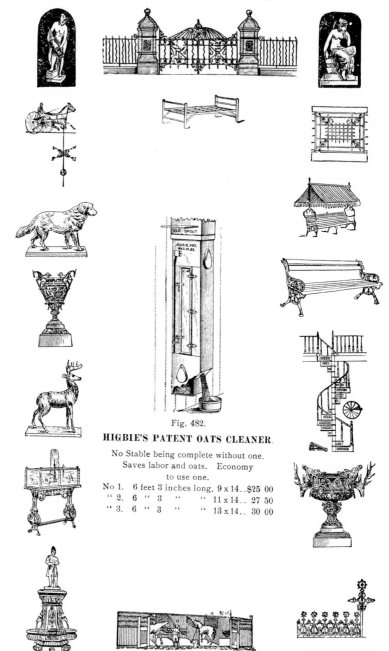

I manufacture a full line of

ORNAMENTAL IRON, ZINC AND BRONZE GOODS,

And illustrate below a few of the different articles, and issue a Separate Catalogue of each line which is furnished gratis upon application.

Fig. 482.

HIGBIE'S PATENT OATS CLEANER.

No Stable being complete without one.
Saves labor and oats.   Economy
to use one.

No 1.   6 feet 3 inches long, 9 x 14 ._ .$25 00
" 2.   6 " 3   "   "   11 x 14 _ . 27 50
" 3.   6 " 3   "   "   13 x 14 _ . 30 00

J. W. FISKE
an historical introduction

Commercial weathervanes reached their zenith in popularity during the last quarter of the nineteenth century at a time when every man was still his own weatherman. The vanes were also popular as a decorative item. Silhouetted against the sky, they were in particular harmony with the romantic architecture of the Victorian era.

Scientific attempts to gather and disseminate information about the weather were initiated in the second half of the nineteenth century by use of the telegraph to transmit data. Napoleon III established the first weather-forecasting system in 1854. By 1870 the United States founded a national weather service as part of the Army Signal Corps. In 1890 a separate civilian Weather Bureau was founded. But until commercial radio brought regular forecasts into the home in the 1920's and 30's, most men depended on their own knowledge and experience to predict the weather.

They relied in part on folk wisdom and their own observations of the heavens, the growth of plant life, and the activity of animals. The sum of their accumulated experience remains in signs and portents that are still familiar today: the red sky in the morning that warns of a coming storm; the aching corns or ring around the moon that foretell rain; the early flight of geese in the fall that promises an early winter; the groundhog and his shadow, predicting the date of the arrival of spring. Beyond using his own eyes and memory, the farmer, the sailor and the merchant could refer to almanacs which had offered compilations of weather lore and predictions since Roman times. He could also refer to a few simple instruments—the weathervane was both the oldest and the most common.

Shifts in wind signal both the timing of seasonal change, and short-range shifts in the weather. With knowledge of local conditions, a man who daily checked the direction of the wind as indicated by the vane could predict, with some accuracy, weather conditions for the immediate future. The principle was evidently known to the Greeks and the Romans. Written descriptions remain of vanes mounted on public and private buildings more than two thousand years ago. The most famous of these ancient wind indicators was the vane in the form of a Triton, mounted on the Tower of the Winds in Athens in 48 B.C.

American weathervanes stem from two primary sources, both of medieval origin. In the ninth century a papal decree called for a cock to be mounted on every church as a reminder of Peter's denial of Christ and the bitter fruit of weak faith. So common did this symbol become that in England the word "weathercock" became synonymous with weathervane. Another form of vane owes its origin to the stiffened heraldic banners flown from the turrets of castles and chateaux, both as identification of their lordly owners and as wind indicators. The distinction between the two types—the figural vane ultimately derived from the cock and the banneret with its roots in heraldry—is preserved in the terminology used in the catalogs of J. W. Fiske and his competitors.

The earliest American weathervanes that have been preserved date back to the late seventeenth century. Known examples represent the traditional form of weathercock and banneret. By the eighteenth century some distinctively American designs had been added to the gallery. An American Indian, with bow and arrow, was mounted on the Province House in Boston in 1716. It was the work of Shem Drowne, one of the few identified eighteenth-century makers of weathervanes. Other Drowne vanes still in place in Boston include a rooster, made in 1721 for the "New Brick" Church and now on the First Church of Cambridge, a banner for "Old North" Church dating from 1740, and a full-bodied grasshopper placed on Fanueil Hall in 1742.

Other indigenous American symbols have patriotic or occupational associations. The former include the enormously popular Federal eagle and various representations of Liberty, as well as more parochial emblems such as the Boston cod. Occupational vanes are even more varied. Excluding those domesticated animals which could be appropriate to farm buildings, there are at least 25 vanes in the 1893 Fiske catalog related to specific business or occupations.

Early American weathervanes are one-of-a-kind products of individual craftsmen, whether carved from wood, wrought in iron, or hammered out of sheet metal. The vast majority of them are two-dimensional silhouettes, although full-bodied examples are not unknown. In quality they range from the crude products of the amateur working at home to the highly sophisticated output of a master craftsman like Drowne.

By the mid-nineteenth century, when the manufacture of commercial vanes became common, the structural and decorative potential of cast iron caused a tremendous expansion of the American metalworking industry. In the 1840's decorative cast-iron trelliswork (now associated with New Orleans, but then common throughout the country) became an enormously popular feature of domestic architecture. Cast iron was also used to front commercial buildings. By the 1850's iron beams, derived from railroad rail, were being used for structural purposes.

At the same time numerous small useful and decorative articles were being produced in cast iron. In 1853, Joseph Winn Fiske, then a young man of 21, left his home in Chelmsford, Mass., to manufacture and sell hardware

A craftsman at the J. W. Fiske weathervane shop smoothing and polishing the soldered seams of an Ethan Allen vane.—*Randall Hagadorn*

and tools in Melbourne, Australia. In 1858 this enterprising fellow returned to Massachusetts and opened a factory for the same purpose. The extent of his early production is revealed in the firm's inclusive 1868 catalog. It ranges from such small items as brackets and hooks, through plant and umbrella stands, to fountains and garden figures, and, of course, weathervanes.

In 1864 Fiske moved his office and showroom to 120 Nassau Street in New York City, but maintained the Massachusetts factory. The building industry in New York was booming, and Fiske soon added ornamental architectural ironwork, settees and chairs, stable fittings, and crestings and finials for mansard roofs to his line. Variety in these lines had become so extensive that separate catalogs were issued for each category.

In 1874, after a second home on Chambers Street, the firm's offices and showrooms were moved to the corner of Park Place and Church Street, an establishment heavily adorned with samples of figures from their weathervanes, fountains, statuary line and furniture. Shortly before the company was incorporated in 1900 as the J. W. Fiske Iron Works, the plant was moved from Massachusetts to Brooklyn. In 1956 the firm moved both office and plant to 111–117 Pennsylvania Ave., Paterson, New Jersey. At the same time its name was changed to J. W. Fiske Architectural Metals, Inc., to reflect technological advances in the metalworking industry. Now operated by the fourth generation of the Fiske family, the company's current production is concentrated on contract architectural metalwork in aluminum, bronze and stainless steel, as well as iron.

The one constant in the firm's production for more than one hundred years of shifting taste and technology has been weathervanes. Although the vanes made by Fiske and their competitors are referred to as "commercial" or "manufactured" vanes, they were, and are, in fact, entirely handmade. The creation of each vane began with the hand-carving of a full-scale wooden model. From this model a cast iron mold was made, and then cut into its component parts. A horse, for example, has separate molds for each side of the body, four legs, head, and tail. Some nineteen of these original molds are still in use at Fiske, including such classics as Ethan Allen, a famous trotter of the 1860's, and other horses, the eagle and arrow, several versions of roosters, and the running deer.

To make a vane, a workman assembles the molds for each component part and fills them with molten lead. When the lead has cooled, he sandwiches a sheet of copper between it and the iron mold, and hammers on the lead to force the copper to conform to the shape of the mold. After the lead form is removed, small details are sharpened by hammer blows shielded by a lead bar. The parts are then soldered together, the seams smoothed and polished, and the figure is mounted on a brass tube, and is ready for painting and gilding.

The high quality of Fiske vanes was recognized almost immediately. In 1866 the company was awarded a bronze medallion and certificate by the American Institute of the City of New York for excellence in the production of copper weathervanes. Nevertheless, Fiske certainly did not enjoy a monopoly in this field, and commercial vanes of high quality were produced by several of its competitors. Only one of Fiske's early competitors, E. G. Washburne of Danvers, Mass., is still in business. In the nineteenth century, however, they were joined in both quality and variety of output by L. W. Cushing & Sons of Waltham, Mass., W. A. Snow & Co. of Boston, and A.B. & W.T. Westervelt of New York, as well as numerous smaller companies. They were gradually replacing the village blacksmith and joiner, and the home handyman as the supplier of metal for useful and decorative objects.

It is often difficult to distinguish among the vanes of these various manufacturers, particularly when they are still perched atop a cupola or roof. Certain motifs were universally popular and were used by most, if not all manufacturers. Among these are the named race horses, based on prints made of well-known favorites by Currier and Ives. For example, although Fiske marks his Ethan Allen as copyrighted in 1893, the vane was produced by several other manufacturers.

Commercial weathervanes were sold both by direct mail and through such outlets as hardware stores. In addition, each manufacturer probably developed special relations with particular architects who would specify that firm's vanes. A number of the buildings for which Fiske supplied vanes were the work of George B. Post, a New York architect. Most of these were probably standard models, but all the makers were prepared to supply custom designs or customized versions based on stock examples. W. A. Snow once

A rich assortment of commercial vanes to be seen today at J. W. Fiske Architectural Metals, Inc., Paterson, N.J.—*Randall Hagadorn*

made a life-size cow and horse for the stock barns of a Maine "potato king" at a cost of $1,500. Fiske's effort for Hinchcliffe's Brewery in Paterson, N.J., was probably less costly. For a corner turret ornament they combined the barrel from the malt shovel and barrel vane, illustrated on page 73, and the screaming eagle usually used for flagpoles or the eagle and scroll vane.

While weathervanes had always served a decorative as well as a useful purpose, they were particularly suited to the forms of Victorian architecture. Architects in the second half of the nineteenth century based the styles of their buildings on a variety of exotic sources. In a romantic era references to distant times and places were calculated to impress, please, and awe. Whether a building was based on a Gothic church, a Renaissance palazzo, or a Moorish castle, there were, however, certain overriding values which governed architectural design and practice. One was a devotion to materials worked, whether by hand or machine, to bring out their intrinsic nature and their highest decorative qualities. Another was the expression of a close relationship between buildings and their natural surroundings. At its best, this was revealed in careful siting and the choice of materials and forms related to the countryside or townscape. At the least, it was expressed in the Victorian preference for "earthy" colors, and in the enjoyment of bay windows, porches, and openwork ornament which provided a free flow of space between the indoors and outdoors.

At the roofline a plethora of crestings, finials and railings often was used to break the sharp transition between building and open sky. Some weathervane manufacturers, including Fiske, produced this related architectural metalwork. And the vanes themselves, swinging freely in the wind, were a fine culmination to such elaborated ornament. The Victorian respect for materials is evident in the great fidelity and fine workmanship applied to such details in the vanes as feathers and fins. Although these motifs would never be visible when the vane was in place, they were rendered with as much care as if it was to be subject to close scrutiny.

Commercial weathervanes, particularly those related to occupations, exemplify the rather simplistic symbolism which was also a mark of the architecture of the era. Although buildings were based on many different sources, sometimes often combined in one structure, certain historical styles were considered most suitable for certain functions. Thus Gothic was appropriate for churches and schools; Roman or Greek for government buildings; and French chateaux for the mansions of *nouveau riche* industrial barons. Such "suitability" appealed particularly to American Victorians, permitting them to make rapid appraisals of status in a fast-growing and rapidly-changing society. So too, occupational vanes enabled the casual observer to identify quickly the function of a number of buildings, and perhaps judge the status of their owners: the cow on the barn of the dairy farmer; the trotter or pacer on a gentleman's stable; the quill on the newspaper office or the editor's house. As will be noted in this catalog, vanes varied greatly in price. Elaborate designs could cost a gentleman farmer a pretty penny, but he would see to it that this sign of his wealth was properly displayed for all to see.

The attention of collectors was first drawn to weathervanes as an aspect of folk art. Certainly the originality and vivacity of a number of the individual vanes is appealing. A simple tulip vane produced by a Pennsylvania Dutchman is a vision of pure and simple delight. In the hands of a master craftsman like Shem Drowne, vanes can almost approach the status of fine art. But appreciation of the freshness of folk art examples should not blind collectors and critics to the high quality of many of the mass-produced vanes.

The anonymous designers and craftsmen who produced the original models for the vane manufacturers were highly skilled and, at their best, genuinely creative. The wonderful open designs of, for instance, the fireman on the ladder in the Fiske catalog, or the tension against the wind of some of the horse and sulky vanes, is as fine as anything produced by individual makers. A number of the designs are infused with awareness of the dramatic effects produced by open silhouettes, swinging freely in the wind, as seen from below.

Expressive of both an ancient tradition, and the technology and craftsmanship of their own era, commercial weathervanes are fine examples of the Victorian minor arts. Recognition of their value, however, is slowly robbing us of their presence along the streets and country roads of America. Hopefully, some will remain in place.

Public collections of commercial weathervanes

The following public historical and art museums have indicated that they do have within their holdings more than one or two nineteenth-century commercial vanes manufactured by J. W. Fiske or other companies. Some of these same museums also possess fine collections of hand-crafted vanes. It is striking to note how few major American museums possess the commercial works. As the reader knows, many of these are highly elaborate and original, and are especially prized by private collectors.

Chicago Historical Society, Chicago, Ill.
Cincinnati Art Museum, Cincinnati, Ohio
Collection of American Art, Arizona State University, Tempe, Ariz.
Henry Ford Museum & Greenfield Village, Dearborn, Mich.
Metropolitan Museum, New York, N.Y.
Missouri Historical Society, St. Louis, Mo.
Museum of Fine Arts, Boston, Mass.
New York Historical Society, New York, N.Y.
New York State Historical Association, Cooperstown, N.Y.
Smithsonian Institution, Fine Arts Museum, Washington, D.C.
Smithsonian Institution, Museum of History and Technology, Washington, D.C.
Shelburne Museum, Shelburne, Vt.

Suggestions for further readings

CHRISTENSEN, ERWIN O. "Weathervanes." *Antiques*, vol. LIX, no. 3, March, 1951, pp. 198–200.

DREPPERD, CARL W. and SMITH, MARJORIE MATTHEWS. *Handbook of Tomorrow's Antiques.* New York: Thomas Y. Crowell, 1953.
   Contains a chapter on vanes.

FITZGERALD, KEN. *Weathervanes and Whirligigs.* New York: Clarkson N. Potter, 1967.

HERTZ, LOUIS H. *Antique Collecting for Men.* New York: Hawthorn, 1969.
   Contains a chapter on vanes.

WHIPPLE, J. RAYNER. "Old New England Weather Vanes." *Old-Time New England* (Bulletin of the Society for the Preservation of New England Antiquities), vol. XXI, no. 2, October, 1940, pp. 45–56. (Reprinted in *Hobbies*, April, 1941, pp. 46–50).

other trade catalogs:

LAWRENCE ROMAINE in *A Guide to American Trade Catalogs, 1744–1900* (New York: R. R. Bowker Co., 1960) lists a number of catalogs issued by weathervane manufacturers. Some of the more relevant are listed below. These listings also include the name of the institution where these catalogs can be found. Unfortunately, they have become very rare items.

CUSHING, L. W. & SONS. Waltham, Mass., 1883. Established 1852. Illustrated catalog #9. Designs of cow, deer, dog, fox, eagle, grasshopper, butterfly, fish, full rigged ship, peacocks, horse—with and without rider and sulky—rooster, sheep, squirrel, key, etc. Sheet and full bodied copper. 20 pages. Available—Metropolitan Museum, New York.

SNOW, W. A. & Co. Boston, Mass., 1889. Illustrated catalog of stable fixtures, garden furniture and ornaments, crestings and weathervanes. 92 pages. Available—Metro-Goldwyn-Mayer, Culver City, Calif., and *Yankee* Magazine Library, Dublin, N.H.

———. 1894. Illustrated catalog of wrought and cast iron work, stable fixtures and fine weathervanes. 148 pages. Available—Metropolitan Museum, New York, N.Y., and Kern County Museum, Bakersfield, Calif.

WESTERVELT, A. B. & W. T. Co. New York, N.Y., 1883. Catalog #6. Vanes for architects, brewers, fire stations, railroads, steamship companies. Such designs as dragons, pens, fire engines, horse cards, locomotives, ships, animals, and the Angel Gabriel. 100 pages. Available—Metropolitan Museum, New York, N.Y.

———. 1884. Similar to 1883. 100 pages. Available—Minnesota Historical Society, St. Paul, Minn.

———. c. 1890. Bannerets, crosses, finials, crestings and weathervanes. Such new designs as Sun Flower, Hook & Ladder, etc. 16 pages. Available—Metropolitan Museum, New York, N.Y.